NEW EDITION

McDougal Littell

Math*Thematics*

Teacher's Resource Book

MODULE 3 Codes

MODULE 4 The Art of Motion

BOOK 2

McDougal Littell
A DIVISION OF HOUGHTON MIFFLIN COMPANY
Evanston, Illinois • Boston • Dallas

Acknowledgments

Writers

The authors of *Math Thematics, Books 1–3,* wish to thank the following writers for their contributions to the *Teacher's Resource Books* for the *Math Thematics* program: Lyle Anderson, Mary Buck, Roslyn Denny, Jean Howard, Deb Johnson, Sallie Morse, Patrick Runkel, Thomas Sanders-Garrett, Bonnie Spence, Christine Tuckerman.

Image Credits

Photography

Front Cover © Cedar Point, Sandusky, Ohio; **3-4** *left Bust of Julius Caesar* (100–44 BC) (marble), Roman. Museo e Gallerie Nazionali di Capodimonte, Naples, Italy. © The Bridgeman Art Library; *right* © Bettmann/Corbis.

Illustration

All art by McDougal Littell/Houghton Mifflin Co.

THE STEM PROJECT *McDougal Littell Math Thematics®* is based on the field-test versions of The STEM Project curriculum. The STEM Project was supported in part by the

 NATIONAL SCIENCE FOUNDATION

under Grant No. ESI-0137682. Opinions expressed in *McDougal Littell Math Thematics®* are those of the authors and not necessarily those of the National Science Foundation.

ISBN-13: 978-0-547-00116-6
ISBN-10: 0-547-00116-9

12345678 9–BHV–11 10 09 08 07

Contents

About the Teacher's Resource Book

In conjunction with the *Math Thematics*, Book 2, Teacher's Edition, this Resource Book contains all of the teaching support that you need to teach Modules 3 and 4.

Blackline Masters

The teaching support in the Resource Books is organized by module and section and includes the following materials:

Warm-Up Exercises Each Warm-Up page is printed in large easy-to-read type and can be used to create an overhead visual or used as a hand-out. Answers for the exercises are provided at the bottom of the page.

Labsheets Blackline masters used in conjunction with various Exploration questions to present data and extend the scope of the Exploration. Answers are provided in the Teacher's Edition.

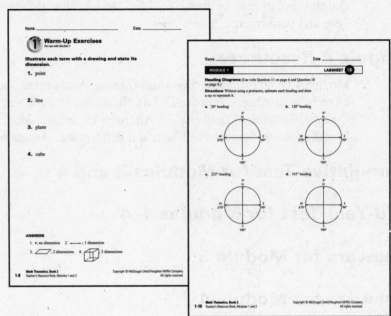

Practice and Applications One to two pages of additional practice for each section in a module, as well as combined practice that covers the whole module.

Study Guide Two to three pages of Study Guide for each section of the module. These Study Guide pages feature key concepts, worked-out examples, and exercises. They can be used for review and reteaching.

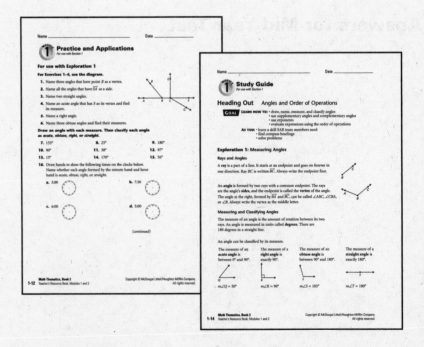

Extended Exploration (E^2) Solution Guide

A comprehensive discussion of the Extended Exploration in the student textbook, including how to assess student responses and performance.

Alternate Extended Exploration (Alternate E^2)

Included in the Teacher's Resource Books for Modules 2, 4, 6, and 7, these extended explorations can be substituted for ones in the student textbook. Materials include teaching notes and assessment procedures.

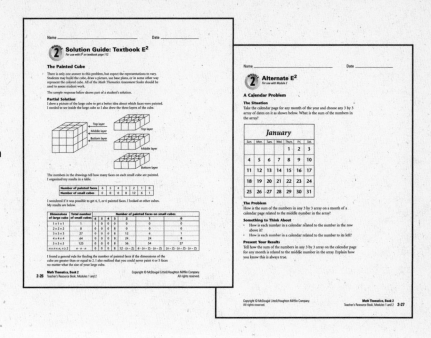

Assessment

Assessment options include a diagnostic module pre-test, quick quizzes for each section, a mid-module quiz, and two module tests, Forms A and B.

Cumulative Test

A cumulative test on both the modules of this Resource Book.

Module Standardized Test

A page of standardized multiple-choice questions for each module.

Module Performance Assessment

A Performance Assessment Task for each module.

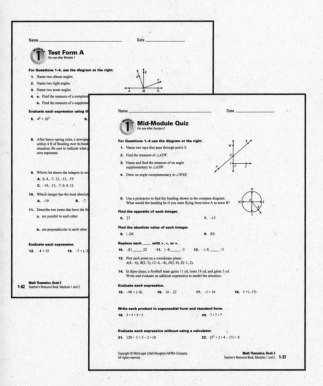

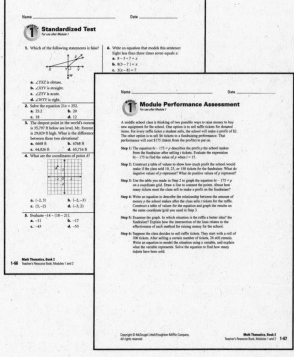

Answers

Complete answers to Practice and Applications, Study Guide, Quick Quizzes, and all Assessments for both modules are provided at the back of this Resource Book.

Contents

Book 2	Teacher's Resources for Module 3

Codes

Name _____   Date _____

3 MODULE **Module Diagnostic Test**
For use before Module 3

1. Which of the following is the approximate circumference of a circle with a   (Sec. 1)
   diameter of 10 cm?

   A. 314.0 cm   **B.** 31.4 cm   **C.** 78.5 cm   **D.** 15.7 cm

2. Tell whether the side lengths 6 in., 3 in., and 3 in. *can* or *cannot* form   (Sec. 1)
   a triangle. Explain how you know.

3. A triangle with side lengths of 7 cm, 8 cm, and 9 cm can be classified as   (Sec. 1)

   A. equilateral.   **B.** isosceles.   **C.** scalene.   **D.** cannot tell from the lengths.

4. Use a compass and straightedge to construct the perpendicular bisector of the   (Sec. 1)
   segment.

5. Which of the following is the prime factorization of 12?   (Sec. 2)

   A. $2^2 \cdot 3$ **B.** $1 \cdot 12$ **C.** $3 \cdot 4$ **D.** 1, 2, 3, 4, 6, and 12

6. Which number is divisible by 2, 3, and 5?   (Sec. 2)

   A. 231   **B.** 620   **C.** 345   **D.** 150

7. What is the greatest common factor of 32 and 12?   (Sec. 2)

   A. 2   **B.** 4   **C.** 96   **D.** 384

8. What is the least common multiple of 6 and 14?   (Sec. 2)

   A. 1   **B.** 2   **C.** 42   **D.** 84

Math Thematics, Book 2
Teacher's Resource Book, Modules 3 and 4

Name _____ Date _____

9. Use <, >, or = to complete the statement $\frac{7}{10}$ ◯ $\frac{4}{9}$. (Sec. 3)

    A. <   **B.** >   **C.** =

10. Which fraction(s) below can be renamed as a mixed number? (Sec. 4)

    A. $\frac{1}{5}$ **B.** $\frac{9}{6}$ **C.** $\frac{6}{12}$ **D.** $\frac{30}{15}$

Find each sum or difference. Write the answer in lowest terms.

11. $\frac{7}{8} - \frac{1}{6}$ (Sec. 3)

12. $5\frac{1}{3} + 4\frac{5}{6}$ (Sec. 4)

13. $5\frac{1}{3} - 3\frac{2}{3}$ (Sec. 4)

14. Measure the length of the segment at right (Sec. 4)

    a. to the nearest inch.
    b. to the nearest half inch.
    c. to the nearest fourth inch.

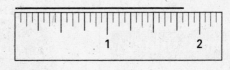

Write the correct measure in each blank. (Sec. 4)

15. 49 in. = _____ yd

16. $1\frac{2}{3}$ yd = _____ ft

The Math Gazette
Codes

Sneak Preview!

Over the next several weeks in our mathematics class, we will be developing and practicing number theory, fractions, geometry, and measurement concepts while completing a thematic unit on *Codes*.

Some of the topics we will be discussing are:

▶ how geometry concepts are used in the design of signal flags

▶ how secret codes built into quilts may have helped 19th century slaves plan escapes

▶ how fractions, mixed numbers, and measurement can be used to help solve cryptograms and guide robots through mazes

Ask Your Student

How can the cipher created by Julius Caesar be used to code and decode secret messages? (Sec. 1)

What is the difference between a composite number and a prime number? (Sec. 2)

How might knowing the approximate number of times the letters of the alphabet are likely to appear help solve a cryptogram? (Sec. 3)

Connections

Literature:
Students will read an excerpt from *Hidden in Plain View* by Jacqueline Tobin. In the book, the daughter of a fugitive slave relates how secret codes were built into quilts. You may enjoy reading the book together.

Social Studies:
Students will explore different uses of codes throughout history. They may be interested in finding out more about the history and development of codes and ciphers. Possible sources include encyclopedias and the internet.

E² Project

Following Section 3, students will have a week to complete the Extended Exploration (E²), *Is There a ... "P"?*. Students will investigate the frequencies of letters in different kinds of writing and develop a letter frequency guide that can be used in different situations. The projects will be evaluated by both the students and the teacher using the assessment scales.

Module Project

After completing the module, students will learn the history of Navajo Code Talkers and use the Navajo language to encode words from the module. Then they will learn about the Huffman code and use prime factorization to create their own codes. A research project will reveal how non-secret codes are used in our daily lives.

Codes

Section Title	Mathematics Students Will Be Learning	Activities
1: Caesar's Cipher	♦ finding the circumference of a circle ♦ classifying and constructing triangles ♦ constructing perpendicular bisectors	♦ build a cipher disk ♦ use a straightedge and compass to construct triangles ♦ explore the *International Code of Signals*
2: Quilt Codes	♦ finding prime factorizations ♦ using divisibility rules ♦ finding greatest common factors and least common multiples	♦ explore number patterns on grids
3: Cryptograms	♦ writing fractions in lowest terms ♦ comparing fractions ♦ adding and subtracting fractions	♦ analyze a cryptogram ♦ explore fraction models
4: Robot Codes	♦ renaming fractions and mixed numbers ♦ adding and subtracting mixed numbers ♦ measuring lengths using customary units ♦ converting between customary units of length	♦ guide a robot through a maze and calculate the distance the robot travels

Activities to do at Home

♦ Work together with your student to solve the following cryptogram. (After Sec. 3)

PATM WBW SXKH LTR MH XBZAM?
GBVX UXEM!

♦ Help your student write a program that will take a robot from the kitchen to the bathroom in your home. The robot should start facing the stove from a point in front of it and end facing the bathroom sink from a point in front of it. Measure the necessary distances in customary units. What is the total distance traveled? (After Sec. 4)

Related Topics

You may want to discuss these related topics with your student:

... _ _ _ ... **Cryptography**

 Signal flags

 Robotics

Name _____   Problem _____

Teacher Assessment Scales
For use with Module 3

☆ *The star indicates that you excelled in some way.*

 Problem Solving

❶ ❷ ❸ ❹ ❺ ☆→

❶ You did not understand the problem well enough to get started or you did not show any work.

❸ You understood the problem well enough to make a plan and to work toward a solution.

❺ You made a plan, you used it to solve the problem, and you verified your solution.

 Mathematical Language

❶ ❷ ❸ ❹ ❺ ☆→

❶ You did not use any mathematical vocabulary or symbols, or you did not use them correctly, or your use was not appropriate.

❸ You used appropriate mathematical language, but the way it was used was not always correct or other terms and symbols were needed.

❺ You used mathematical language that was correct and appropriate to make your meaning clear.

 Representations

❶ ❷ ❸ ❹ ❺ ☆→

❶ You did not use any representations such as equations, tables, graphs, or diagrams to help solve the problem or explain your solution.

❸ You made appropriate representations to help solve the problem or help you explain your solution, but they were not always correct or other representations were needed.

❺ You used appropriate and correct representations to solve the problem or explain your solution.

 Connections

❶ ❷ ❸ ❹ ❺ ☆→

❶ You attempted or solved the problem and then stopped.

❸ You found patterns and used them to extend the solution to other cases, or you recognized that this problem relates to other problems, mathematical ideas, or applications.

❺ You extended the ideas in the solution to the general case, or you showed how this problem relates to other problems, mathematical ideas, or applications.

 Presentation

❶ ❷ ❸ ❹ ❺ ☆→

❶ The presentation of your solution and reasoning is unclear to others.

❸ The presentation of your solution and reasoning is clear in most places, but others may have trouble understanding parts of it.

❺ The presentation of your solution and reasoning is clear and can be understood by others.

Content Used: _____   **Computational Errors:**   Yes ☐   No ☐

Notes on Errors: _____

Name _____   Problem _____

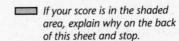 If your score is in the shaded area, explain why on the back of this sheet and stop.

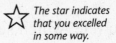 The star indicates that you excelled in some way.

 Problem Solving

1 I did not understand the problem well enough to get started or I did not show any work.

3 I understood the problem well enough to make a plan and to work toward a solution.

5 I made a plan, I used it to solve the problem, and I verified my solution.

 Mathematical Language

1 I did not use any mathematical vocabulary or symbols, or I did not use them correctly, or my use was not appropriate.

3 I used appropriate mathematical language, but the way it was used was not always correct or other terms and symbols were needed.

5 I used mathematical language that was correct and appropriate to make my meaning clear.

 Representations

1 I did not use any representations such as equations, tables, graphs, or diagrams to help solve the problem or explain my solution.

3 I made appropriate representations to help solve the problem or help me explain my solution, but they were not always correct or other representations were needed.

5 I used appropriate and correct representations to solve the problem or explain my solution.

 Connections

1 I attempted or solved the problem and then stopped.

3 I found patterns and used them to extend the solution to other cases, or I recognized that this problem relates to other problems, mathematical ideas, or applications.

5 I extended the ideas in the solution to the general case, or I showed how this problem relates to other problems, mathematical ideas, or applications.

 Presentation

1 The presentation of my solution and reasoning is unclear to others.

3 The presentation of my solution and reasoning is clear in most places, but others may have trouble understanding parts of it.

5 The presentation of my solution and reasoning is clear and can be understood by others.

Name _____   Date _____

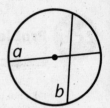

1. In the circle, which segment is a diameter?
Explain how you know.

2. Round each number to the individual place value.

   a. 4.293; tenths

   b. 3.14159; hundredths

   c. 32.511; whole number

3. State two properties of triangles.

ANSWERS

1. *a*; it is a segment with both endpoints on the circle and it passes through the
center.   2. a. 4.3 b. 3.14 c. 33   3. Sample Response: They have 3 sides; they
have 3 angles; triangles can be classified by their angles as acute, obtuse, or right.

Name _____ Date _____

Practice and Applications

For use with Section 1

For use with Exploration 1

1. Find the circumference of each circle with the given diameter. Use 3.14 or the ⟦π⟧ key on a calculator. Round each answer to the nearest hundredth.

    a. 6 m   **b.** 28 cm   **c.** 34 ft

    d. 18 in.   **e.** 6.3 cm   **f.** 8.2 m

    g. 1.5 ft   **h.** 42 in.   **i.** 17.1 m

2. A circular painting has a radius of $5\frac{1}{2}$ in. What is the circumference of the painting? Use 3.14 or the ⟦π⟧ key on a calculator. Round the answer to the nearest hundredth.

For use with Exploration 2

3. Use a compass and a ruler to construct each triangle. Label the sides with their lengths.

    a. an isosceles triangle with sides of length 5 in., 5 in., and 6 in.

    b. a scalene triangle with sides of length 2 in., 4 in., and 5 in.

    c. an equilateral triangle with sides of length $2\frac{1}{2}$ in.

4. Tell whether each set of side lengths *can* or *cannot* form a triangle. If they can, tell whether the triangle is *isosceles*, *equilateral*, or *scalene*.

    a. 7 cm, 9 cm, 12 cm   **b.** 18 in., 18 in., 23 in.

    c. 8 km, 15 km, 24 km   **d.** 31 in., 31 in., 22 in.

    e. 3.8 m, 3.8 m, 3.8 m   **f.** 6.5 in., 7.3 in., 15 in.

    g. 4.1 ft, 5.8 ft, 6.2 ft   **h.** $2\frac{1}{2}$ ft, $4\frac{1}{4}$ ft, 8 ft

5. An artist is etching an isosceles triangle in a metal plate. The lengths of two of the sides of the triangle are 4 cm long. Which length *cannot* be the length of the third side of the triangle: 4 cm, 6.9 cm or 11 cm?

(continued)

MODULE 3 Practice and Applications
For use with Section 1

6. Classify each triangle as *acute*, *obtuse*, or *right*.

a.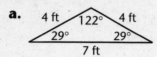

b.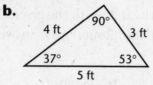

c.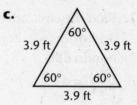

d.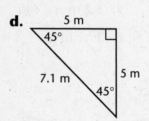

e.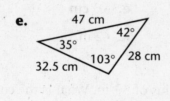

In Exercises 7–9, use a ruler.

7. Name the perpendicular bisector of $\overline{AC}$.

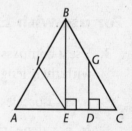

8. Which two segments are the perpendicular bisectors of each other?

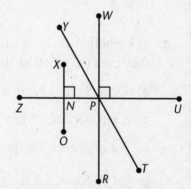

9. Name the perpendicular bisector of diameter $\overline{UN}$. Choose one of the other segments and explain why it is *not* the perpendicular bisector of $\overline{UN}$.

Name _____ Date _____

Caesar's Cipher   Triangles, Circles, and Constructions

GOAL   **LEARN HOW TO:** • find the circumference of a circle
• classify triangles by their side lengths and by the measures of their angles
• construct triangles
• determine which side lengths will form a triangle

AS YOU: • build a cipher disk
• examine flags

Exploration 1: The Cipher Disk

Parts of a Circle

A circle can be constructed using a compass. A **circle** is the set of all points in a plane that are the same distance from a given point called the **center**. A segment drawn from the center of a circle to any point on the circle is called a **radius**. A **chord** is a segment that has both endpoints on a circle. Any chord that passes through the center of its circle is a **diameter** of that circle. An **arc** like $\overset{\frown}{AB}$ is part of a circle.

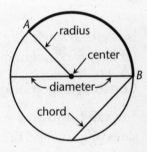

Circumference

The words *radius* and *diameter* are also used to refer to the lengths of these segments. **Circumference** is the distance around a circle. The relationship between the circumference, C, of a circle and its diameter, d, is given by

$$\pi = \frac{C}{d} \text{ or } C = \pi d.$$

The value of the constant π (read "pi") is about 3.14.

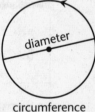

circumference

Example

Find the circumference of a circle with radius 8 ft. Use 3.14 for π.

Sample Response

$d = 2r$ ← Find the diameter d. The diameter is twice the radius.
$\quad = 2(8)$ ← Substitute 8 for r.
$\quad = 16$ ft

$C = \pi d$
$\quad = 3.14(16)$ ← Substitute 3.14 for π and 16 for d.
$\quad = 50.24$ ft

The circumference of the circle is approximately 50.24 ft.

Study Guide
For use with Section 1

Exploration 2: Flag Codes

Classifying Triangles by Side Length

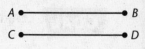

Two segments equal in length are **congruent**. In the figure, segments *AB* and *CD* are congruent. This is written $\overline{AB} \cong \overline{CD}$.

Triangles can be classified by their sides. Triangles with at least two sides congruent are **isosceles triangles.** Triangles with three congruent sides are **equilateral triangles.** Triangles with no congruent sides are **scalene triangles.**

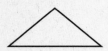

Isosceles Triangle
(at least two congruent sides)

Equilateral Triangle
(three congruent sides)

Scalene Triangle
(no congruent sides)

Constructing Triangles

You can construct a triangle using a compass and a ruler. For every pair of sides of a triangle, the sum of their lengths must be greater than the length of the third side.

Example

a. Can a 2 in. segment, a 3 in. segment, and a 7 in. segment form a triangle?

b. Can a 3 cm segment, a 4 cm segment, and a 5 cm segment form a triangle?

Sample Response

a. Since 2 + 3 < 7, a triangle cannot be formed.

b. Since 3 + 4 > 5, 4 + 5 > 3, and 3 + 5 > 4, a triangle can be formed.

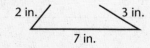   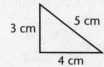

Name _____   Date _____

Classifying Triangles by Angle Measure

Triangles can also be classified by the measures of their angles. A triangle that has only acute angles is an **acute triangle**. An **obtuse triangle** has one obtuse angle. A **right triangle** has one right angle.

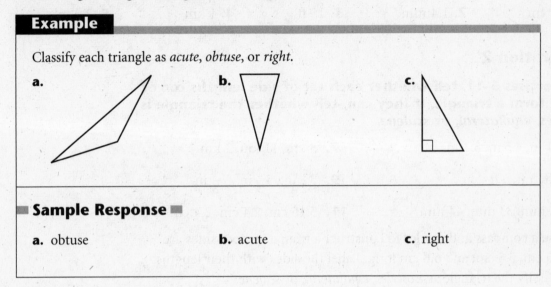

Example

Classify each triangle as *acute*, *obtuse*, or *right*.

a.

b.

c.

Sample Response

a. obtuse   b. acute   c. right

Perpendicular Bisectors

A **perpendicular bisector** of a segment is a line that is perpendicular to the segment and divides it into two congruent segments.

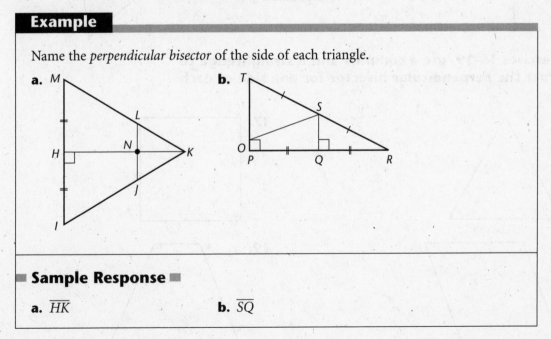

Example

Name the *perpendicular bisector* of the side of each triangle.

a.

b.

Sample Response

a. $\overline{HK}$ b. $\overline{SQ}$

Name _____   Date _____

Study Guide: Practice & Application Exercises

For use with Section 1

Exploration 1

Find the circumference of each circle with the given diameter. If necessary, round each answer to the nearest hundredth. Use 3.14 or the π key on a calculator.

1. 12 cm   **2.** 1.4 mm   **3.** 15 ft   **4.** 1 km   **5.** 2.3 m

Exploration 2

For Exercises 6–11, tell whether each set of side lengths *can* or *cannot* form a triangle. If they can, tell whether the triangle is *isosceles*, *equilateral*, or *scalene*.

6. 3.1 m, 4.5 m, 3.1 m

7. 8 km, 11 km, 2 km

8. 5 ft, 5 ft, 5 ft

9. $5\frac{1}{2}$ in., $3\frac{2}{3}$ in., $7\frac{1}{8}$ in.

10. 22 mm, 33 mm, 44 mm

11. 5.16 cm, 2.4 cm, 2.4 cm

12. Use a compass and a ruler to construct a triangle whose sides are 4.5 cm, 5.5 cm, and 6.6 cm long. Label the sides with their lengths. Classify the triangle as *isosceles*, *equilateral*, or *scalene*.

Classify each triangle as *acute*, *obtuse*, or *right*.

13.   **14.** 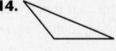   **15.**

For Exercises 16–19, use a compass and a straightedge to construct the perpendicular bisector for one side of each figure.

16.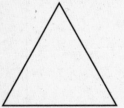

17.

18.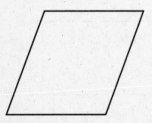

19.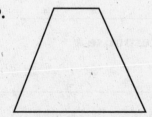

Name _____ Date _____

1. Construct a scalene triangle with side lengths of 8 cm, 6 cm, and 4 cm.

2. Can side lengths of 3 in., 3 in., and 9 in. form a triangle? If they can, tell whether the triangle is *isosceles*, *scalene*, or *equilateral*. If not, explain why not.

3. Find the circumference of a circle with each measure. Use 3.14 for π.

   a. $r = 4$ ft

   b. $d = 70$ in.

4. Construct the perpendicular bisector of the line segment below.

Name _____ Date _____

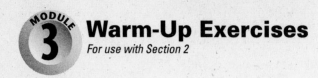

Warm-Up Exercises
For use with Section 2

Multiply.

1. 6 • 120

2. 15 • 48

3. 30 • 24

Divide.

4. 256 ÷ 8

5. 256 ÷ 16

6. 256 ÷ 4

ANSWERS

1. 720   2. 720   3. 720   4. 32   5. 16   6. 64

MODULE 3   LABSHEET **2A**

10 × 10 Grid (Use with Questions 3–5 on page 176 and Questions 7 and 9 on page 177.)

You will need: Orange, red, yellow, green, and blue colored pencils or markers.

Directions

1. Mark an X through the number 1. Use orange to color the diamond in which the 2 is located.

2. Use **red** to color the upper-left corner of the key and the upper-left corner of all squares containing a number that is divisible by 2.

3. The next uncolored square is 3. Color the diamond in which the 3 is located **orange**. Use **yellow** to color the upper-right corner of the key and the upper-right corner of all squares containing a number that is divisible by 3.

4. Repeat this process for 5 and 7. Color the diamonds in which the numbers are located **orange**. Use **green** to color the lower-right corners of the key and all of the squares containing a number that is divisible by 5. Use **blue** to color the lower-left corners of the key and of all the squares containing a number that is divisible by 7.

1	2	3	4	5	6	7	8	9	10
11	12	13	14	15	16	17	18	19	20
21	22	23	24	25	26	27	28	29	30
31	32	33	34	35	36	37	38	39	40
41	42	43	44	45	46	47	48	49	50
51	52	53	54	55	56	57	58	59	60
61	62	63	64	65	66	67	68	69	70
71	72	73	74	75	76	77	78	79	80
81	82	83	84	85	86	87	88	89	90
91	92	93	94	95	96	97	98	99	100

MODULE 3   LABSHEET **2B**

Circle Grid (Use with Questions 14 and 15 on pages 179–180.)

Complete the grid by writing numbers in the circles following the arrow directions.

⟶ × 2   ↓ × 3

1. To complete the first row, begin at the circle containing the number 1.

   a. $1 \times 2 = 2$, so write a 2 in the circle to the right of the one containing 1.

   b. $2 \times 2 = 4$, so write a 4 in the circle to the right of the one containing 2.

   c. Continue in the same way until all the circles in the first row are filled.

2. To complete the first column, begin at the circle containing the number 1.

   a. $1 \times 3 = 3$, so write a 3 in the circle below the one containing 1.

   b. $3 \times 3 = 9$, so write a 9 in the circle below the one containing 3.

   c. Continue in the same way until all the circles in the first column are filled.

3. To complete the remainder of the grid, follow the same patterns you used in the first row and column, beginning at one of the circles you have already filled.

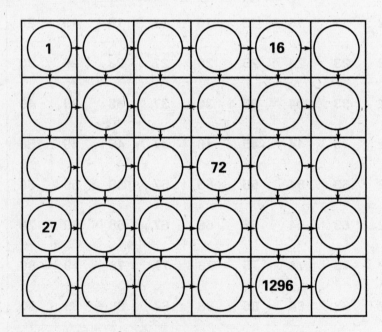

MODULE 3   LABSHEET **2C**

Divisibility-by-Nine Table (Use with Question 17 on page 180.)

Directions Complete the table and look for a pattern involving the sum of the digits.

Number divisible by 9	Digits in the number	Sum of the digits
18	1, 8	
27	2, 7	$2 + 7 = 9$
54	5, 4	$5 + 4 = 9$
918	9, 1, 8	
2457	2, 4, 5, 7	$2 + 4 + 5 + 7 = 18$
9153		
71,127,207	7, 1, 1, 2, 7, 2, 0, 7	

7 × 7 Grid (Use with Questions 24–26 on page 182.)

1	2	3	4	5	6	7
8	9	10	11	12	13	14
15	16	17	18	19	20	21
22	23	24	25	26	27	28
29	30	31	32	33	34	35
36	37	38	39	40	41	42
43	44	45	46	47	48	49

Name _____ Date _____

Practice and Applications
For use with Section 2

For use with Exploration 1

1. Find all the factors of each number.

    a. 10   **b.** 14   **c.** 18

    d. 62   **e.** 81   **f.** 98

    g. 125   **h.** 169   **i.** 230

2. Tell whether each number is *prime* or *composite*.

    a. 5   **b.** 14   **c.** 17

    d. 26   **e.** 27   **f.** 35

    g. 49   **h.** 61   **i.** 55

3. Find the prime factorization of each number.

    a. 18   **b.** 24   **c.** 27

    d. 35   **e.** 38   **f.** 40

    g. 125   **h.** 110   **i.** 150

4. Tour Bus A has 42 people and Tour Bus B has 36 people. The two buses are going to a historic mansion together. At the mansion the people will be divided into smaller groups to go on guided tours. Each group must contain people from both buses, and the people from each bus must be divided evenly among the groups.

    a. List all the possible ways the groups can be set up.

    b. The mansion limits the size of each tour group to a maximum of 15 people. Which groups will be allowed on the tours?

5. For each rectangle:
Find the area and the perimeter.
Find the length and width of a rectangle with the same area and a smaller perimeter.
Find the length and width of a rectangle with the same area and a greater perimeter.

    a. [rectangle] 2 in.   9 in.   **b.** [rectangle] 2 m   16 m   **c.** [rectangle] 2 ft   10 ft

(continued)

Name _____ Date _____

Practice and Applications
For use with Section 2

For use with Exploration 2

6. Tell whether each number is divisible by each of the numbers 2, 3, 4, 5, 6, 9, and 10.

a. 35	**b.** 44	**c.** 118
d. 138	**e.** 141	**f.** 225
g. 279	**h.** 350	**i.** 371
j. 420	**k.** 608	**l.** 685

7. Find the greatest common factor of each group of numbers.

a. 12, 24	**b.** 16, 36	**c.** 20, 45
d. 15, 24	**e.** 12, 25	**f.** 14, 42
g. 54, 126	**h.** 50, 125	**i.** 16, 20, 30
j. 9, 18, 21	**k.** 18, 24, 32	**l.** 60, 84, 108
m. 72, 88, 136	**n.** 55, 121, 132	**o.** 28, 42, 84

8. Mr. Brown has $76.50. She wants to distribute the money evenly between her 2 nieces and 4 nephews. Can she do this? Explain.

For use with Exploration 3

9. Find the least common multiple of each group of numbers.

a. 4, 5	**b.** 12, 20	**c.** 18, 10
d. 15, 25	**e.** 64, 16	**f.** 3, 8, 12
g. 54, 126	**h.** 50, 125	**i.** 16, 20, 30
j. 9, 18, 21	**k.** 18, 24, 32	**l.** 60, 84, 108

10. The price for one type of balloon is $0.16. Another type costs $0.20 per balloon. Suppose the same amount of money is spent on each type.

a. What is the least total amount that can be spent?

b. How many of each type of balloon are there when you spend the least total amount?

Name _____ Date _____

Study Guide
For use with Section 2

Quilt Codes   Factors, Divisibility, and Multiples

GOAL   **LEARN HOW TO:** • find factors
• find the prime factorization of a number
• use divisibility rules to find factors
• find the greatest common factor of two or more numbers
• find the least common multiple of two or more numbers

AS YOU: • explore number patterns on a grid
• explore a circle grid
• work with a number grid

Exploration 1: Prime Factorization

A **factor** is a number that divides another number with no remainder. A number is **divisible** by another number when it can be divided by that number without leaving a remainder.

The *factors* of 12 are 1, 2, 3, 4, 6, and 12.

12 is *divisible* by 1, 2, 3, 4, 6, and 12.

A **prime** number has only two factors, 1 and itself. A **composite** number has more than two factors. 0 and 1 are neither prime nor composite.

5 is *prime* because its only factors are 1 and 5.

12 is a *composite* number.

The **prime factorization** of a number is the product of its prime factors.

Example

a. Find all the factors of 20.

b. Tell if 20 is *prime* or *composite*.

c. Write the prime factorization of 20.

Sample Response

a. Start a list with 1 and the number 20. Then think of all the other pairs of factors.

$1 \cdot 20 = 20, 2 \cdot 10 = 20,$ and $4 \cdot 5 = 20$

The factors of 20 are 1, 2, 4, 5, 10, and 20.

b. Since there are more than two factors, 20 is a *composite* number.

c. Use a factor tree to find the prime factors of 20.

```
      20
     /  \
    2    10
    |   /  \
   (2)(2) (5)
```

The prime factorization of 20 is $2 \cdot 2 \cdot 5$, or $2^2 \cdot 5$.

Name _____ Date _____

 **Study Guide**
For use with Section 2

Exploration 2: Common Factors

Divisibility and Common Factors

To find some factors of a number, you can use **divisibility rules**.

A number is divisible by:

- 2, if the ones digit is even.
- 3, if the sum of the digits is divisible by 3.
- 4, if the number formed by the tens and ones digits is divisible by 4.
- 5, if the ones digit is 0 or 5.
- 6, if it is divisible by both 2 and 3.
- 9, if the sum of the digits is divisible by 9.
- 10, if the ones digit is a 0.

The **greatest common factor (GCF)** of two or more numbers is the greatest factor that is common to those numbers.

Example
Find the GCF of 12 and 20.

■ Sample Response ■

Make separate lists of the factors. Identify the greatest factors in *both* lists.

factors of 12: **1**, **2**, 3, **4**, 6, 12
factors of 20: **1**, **2**, **4**, 5, 20 } common factors: 1, 2, 4

The GCF of 12 and 20 is 4.

Exploration 3: Common Multiples

Multiples

A **multiple** of a whole number is the product of that number and any nonzero whole number.

The **least common multiple (LCM)** of two or more numbers is the least number that is a multiple of each number. For example, to find the LCM of 12 and 20, make partial lists of the multiples until the first common multiple appears.

multiples of 12: 12, 24, 36, 48, **60**, 72, …   multiples of 20: 20, 40, **60**, 80, 100, …

The LCM of 12 and 20 is 60.

Math Thematics, Book 2
Teacher's Resource Book, Modules 3 and 4

Name _____   Date _____

 Study Guide: Practice & Application Exercises
MODULE 3

For use with Section 2

3-25 (top right corner)

Exploration 1

Find all the factors of each number.

1. 15   **2.** 63   **3.** 140   **4.** 216

5. Which of the following numbers is *not* a factor of 100?

   A. 5   **B.** 10   **C.** 15   **D.** 20

Tell whether each number is *prime* or *composite*. If a number is composite, write its prime factorization.

6. 17   **7.** 47   **8.** 34   **9.** 343

10. 96   **11.** 89   **12.** 113   **13.** 147

Exploration 2

Tell whether each number is divisible by each of the numbers 2, 3, 4, 5, 6, 9, and 10.

14. 88   **15.** 405   **16.** 540   **17.** 435

18. 162   **19.** 500   **20.** 576   **21.** 625

Find the greatest common factor of each group of numbers.

22. 45, 150   **23.** 60, 70, 80   **24.** 23, 53

25. 45, 81, 117   **26.** 42, 112   **27.** 63, 105

Exploration 3

Find the least common multiple of each group of numbers.

28. 3, 9   **29.** 24, 30   **30.** 5, 15, 45

31. Small gumballs cost 15¢ each. Big gumballs cost 25¢ each. If Aaron wants to spend the same amount of money on both sizes, what is the least number of gumballs he will have to buy? Explain how you found your answer.

Name _____ Date _____

 **Quick Quiz**
For use after Section 2

1. Find all the factors of 240.

2. Is 87 *prime* or *composite*?

3. Find the prime factorization of 720. Write the prime factorization using exponents.

4. Tell whether 1836 is divisible by 2, 3, 4, 5, 6, 9, or 10.

5. Find the greatest common factor and the least common multiple of 48, 60, and 84.

Math Thematics, Book 2
Teacher's Resource Book, Modules 3 and 4

Name _____ Date _____

Mid-Module Quiz
For use after Section 2

Use 3.14 or the □ **key on a calculator to find the circumference of a circle with each measure. Round answers to the nearest tenth.**

1. radius = 18 mm

2. diameter = 16 mi

Tell whether each set of side lengths *can* or *cannot* form a triangle. If they can, tell whether the triangle is *isosceles*, *scalene*, or *equilateral*.

3. 6 in., 5 in., 6 in.

4. 15 cm, 7 cm, 8 cm

5. Construct an equilateral triangle with the given side.

_____

6. Construct the perpendicular bisector of $\overline{AB}$.

7. Find all the factors of 82.

8. Is 171 *prime* or *composite*? Explain.

9. Write the prime factorization of 495.

10. Tell whether 102,330 is divisible by 2, 3, 4, 5, 6, 9, or 10.

11. Find the greatest common factor (GCF) of 16, 40, and 120.

12. Find the least common multiple (LCM) of 16, 40, and 120.

3 Warm-Up Exercises

For use with Section 3

Write the fraction represented by the shading in each figure.

1.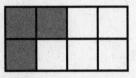

2.

3.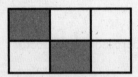

4.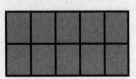

5.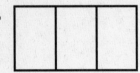

ANSWERS

1. $\frac{1}{4}$ 2. $\frac{3}{8}$ 3. $\frac{2}{6}$ or $\frac{1}{3}$ 4. $\frac{10}{10}$ or 1   5. $\frac{0}{3}$ or 0

Name _____   Date _____

Equivalent Fraction Models (Use with Question 16 on page 194 and Question 17 on page 195.)

Directions For each equation, find the equivalent fractions, shade the equivalent amounts, and complete the equations to find the sum or difference.

a.

$\dfrac{1}{2}$ + $\dfrac{1}{5}$ =   _____

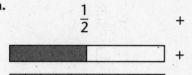   +   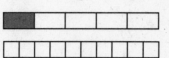   =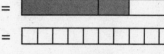

$\dfrac{\square}{10}$ + $\dfrac{\square}{10}$ = $\dfrac{\square}{10}$

b.

$\dfrac{2}{3}$ − $\dfrac{1}{4}$ =   _____

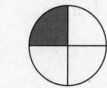   −   =

    −   =

$\dfrac{\square}{12}$ − $\dfrac{\square}{12}$ = $\dfrac{\square}{12}$

c.

$\dfrac{1}{3}$ + $\dfrac{1}{8}$ =   _____

   +   =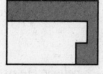

   +   =

$\dfrac{\square}{24}$ + $\dfrac{\square}{24}$ = $\dfrac{\square}{24}$

Practice and Applications
For use with Section 3

For use with Exploration 1

1. Write each fraction in lowest terms.

   a. $\frac{4}{16}$ b. $\frac{18}{27}$ c. $\frac{15}{35}$

   d. $\frac{6}{9}$ e. $\frac{12}{20}$ f. $\frac{25}{30}$

   g. $\frac{42}{77}$ h. $\frac{21}{36}$ i. $\frac{18}{81}$

2. Tell whether each fraction is *greater than* or *less than* $\frac{1}{2}$.

   a. $\frac{11}{19}$ b. $\frac{14}{30}$ c. $\frac{63}{130}$

3. Tell whether each fraction is closest to 0, $\frac{1}{2}$, or 1.

   a. $\frac{1}{12}$ b. $\frac{5}{8}$ c. $\frac{8}{9}$

   d. $\frac{3}{7}$ e. $\frac{2}{15}$ f. $\frac{9}{10}$

4. Replace each ___?___ with >, <, or =.

   a. $\frac{4}{5}$ __?__ $\frac{4}{15}$ b. $\frac{7}{8}$ __?__ $\frac{8}{9}$ c. $\frac{2}{5}$ __?__ $\frac{2}{3}$

   d. $\frac{8}{15}$ __?__ $\frac{64}{120}$ e. $\frac{11}{12}$ __?__ $\frac{23}{27}$ f. $\frac{19}{37}$ __?__ $\frac{41}{95}$

For use with Exploration 2

5. Find each sum or difference. Write each answer in lowest terms.

   a. $\frac{1}{4} + \frac{3}{5}$ b. $\frac{5}{8} + \frac{1}{4}$ c. $\frac{5}{12} + \frac{3}{8}$

   d. $\frac{7}{10} - \frac{3}{5}$ e. $\frac{8}{9} - \frac{5}{12}$ f. $\frac{7}{8} - \frac{1}{2}$

6. Kim has $\frac{3}{4}$ c celery. He uses $\frac{3}{8}$ c celery to make a tuna salad. He uses $\frac{1}{6}$ c celery to make a sauce. How much celery does Kim have left?

Name _____ Date _____

Study Guide
For use with Section 3

Cryptograms Fractions

GOAL **LEARN HOW TO:** • write fractions in lowest terms
                                • compare fractions using least common denominators
                                • add and subtract fractions with unlike denominators

                 AS YOU: • analyze a cryptogram
                             • explore fraction models

Exploration 1: Comparing Fractions

Comparing Fractions

The **least common denominator** of two fractions is the least common multiple of their denominators. Fractions can be compared by renaming them as equivalent fractions using the least common denominator.

Example

Compare $\frac{3}{4}$ and $\frac{5}{7}$.

Sample Response

The LCM of 4 and 7 is 28. So the least common denominator of $\frac{3}{4}$ and $\frac{5}{7}$ is 28.

Rename each fraction as an equivalent fraction with the common denominator.

$\frac{3}{4} = \frac{3 \cdot 7}{4 \cdot 7} = \frac{21}{28}$ and $\frac{5}{7} = \frac{5 \cdot 4}{7 \cdot 4} = \frac{20}{28}$

Compare the fractions that have the same denominator.

$\frac{21}{28} > \frac{20}{28}$, so $\frac{3}{4} > \frac{5}{7}$

Study Guide
For use with Section 3

Lowest Terms

A fraction is written in **lowest terms** when the greatest common factor of the numerator and denominator is 1.

Example

Write $\frac{36}{81}$ in lowest terms.

Sample Response

Make lists of the factors of the numerator and denominator. Identify the common factors.

  factors of 36: **1**, 2, **3**, 4, 6, **9**, 12, 18, 36

  factors of 81: **1**, **3**, **9**, 27, 81

The GCF of 36 and 81 is 9.

Divide both the numerator and denominator by their GCF, 9.

$$\frac{36}{81} = \frac{36 \div 9}{81 \div 9} = \frac{4}{9}$$

Exploration 2: Adding and Subtracting Fractions

Adding and Subtracting Fractions

You can add or subtract fractions by using a common denominator.

Example

Find $\frac{2}{5} + \frac{3}{8}$.

Sample Response

The LCM of 5 and 8 is 40. So, the least common denominator of $\frac{2}{5}$ and $\frac{3}{8}$ is 40.

Rename each fraction as an equivalent fraction with the common denominator.

$$\frac{2}{5} = \frac{2 \cdot 8}{5 \cdot 8} = \frac{16}{40} \quad \text{and} \quad \frac{3}{8} = \frac{3 \cdot 5}{8 \cdot 5} = \frac{15}{40}$$

Add the equivalent fractions and simplify if possible.

$$\frac{16}{40} + \frac{15}{40} = \frac{31}{40}, \text{ so } \frac{2}{5} + \frac{3}{8} = \frac{31}{40}$$

Name _____   Date _____

Study Guide: Practice & Application Exercises
For use with Section 3

Exploration 1

Write each fraction in lowest terms.

1. $\frac{6}{18}$　　　　　　2. $\frac{21}{27}$　　　　　　3. $\frac{240}{360}$

4. $\frac{35}{55}$　　　　　　5. $\frac{3}{33}$　　　　　　6. $\frac{52}{78}$

7. $\frac{40}{88}$　　　　　　8. $\frac{9}{43}$　　　　　　9. $\frac{56}{80}$

Choosing a Method **Tell whether you would use *mental math*, *estimation*, or *paper-and-pencil* to compare each pair of fractions. Then replace each ___?___ with >, <, or =.**

10. $\frac{3}{11}$ __?__ $\frac{3}{8}$　　　　11. $\frac{4}{13}$ __?__ $\frac{9}{13}$　　　　12. $\frac{6}{35}$ __?__ $\frac{3}{7}$

13. $\frac{3}{15}$ __?__ $\frac{4}{10}$　　　　14. $\frac{3}{18}$ __?__ $\frac{2}{9}$　　　　15. $\frac{8}{36}$ __?__ $\frac{7}{30}$

Exploration 2

Find each sum or difference. Write each answer in lowest terms.

16. $\frac{8}{12} - \frac{2}{3}$　　　　17. $\frac{4}{5} + \frac{2}{45}$　　　　18. $\frac{11}{18} - \frac{3}{15}$

19. $\frac{4}{5} - \frac{2}{15}$　　　　20. $\frac{3}{4} + \frac{1}{6}$　　　　21. $\frac{7}{8} - \frac{7}{20}$

22. $\frac{17}{44} + \frac{5}{33}$　　　　23. $\frac{7}{10} + \frac{2}{15}$　　　　24. $\frac{17}{18} - \frac{7}{27}$

25. Adam read $\frac{3}{13}$ of a novel on Thursday night and $\frac{16}{39}$ of the novel on Friday night. What fraction of the novel did Adam read on these two nights?

Name _____   Date _____

Quick Quiz
For use after Section 3

1. Write $\frac{42}{72}$ in lowest terms.

2. Which is greater, $\frac{4}{9}$ or $\frac{17}{40}$?

3. Graph these fractions on a number line. Then list them in numerical order from least to greatest.

$$\frac{7}{16} \quad \frac{1}{2} \quad \frac{3}{8} \quad \frac{3}{4} \quad \frac{1}{16}$$

4. Find the sum $\frac{1}{15} + \frac{1}{3} + \frac{3}{5}$.

5. Find the difference $\frac{8}{9} - \frac{2}{5}$.

Name _____ Date _____

Solution Guide: Textbook E²
For use with E² on textbook page 201

Is There a . . . "P"?

All of the *Math Thematics Assessment Scales* could be used to assess students' work. There are several solutions to this problem. Guides may give general information regarding the frequencies of letters, naming letters that occur *more than* $\frac{3}{4}$, *about* $\frac{1}{2}$, or *less than* $\frac{1}{4}$ of the time in a given length of text. Or guides might give a specific percent for each letter of the alphabet or give the number of times on average each letter occurred in texts of 100 words.

The sample response below shows part of a student's solution.

Partial Solution

I began this problem by randomly selecting different pages from my social studies book. I marked off passages of 100 letters and recorded the frequency of each letter that occurred. Then for each letter of the alphabet I found the average of the frequencies I had recorded. I tested my new guide on a page from my library book and it was not exact, but pretty close.

I noticed that the consonants R, S, T, L, and N appeared frequently in the samples I took, so that is probably why those letters are given to contestants on the *Wheel of Fortune*. In the original version of the game, contestants were not given any letters and most of them tended to always pick these same ones and it got boring to watch. Now the contestants are given R, S, T, L, N, E and forced to pick 3 more consonants and a vowel, which makes it a little more interesting.

In some of my samples, the vowel A occurred just as much as the vowel E. I think that maybe a different guide would be needed for a book of medical terms or for a book written in another language such as French or Spanish.

Letter frequencies tend to vary depending on the text used as a sample. The list below shows frequencies in a sample of 816 letters. Poems, essays, and scientific texts were used to create the list. (Source: Churchhouse, Robert. *Codes and Ciphers: Julius Caesar, the Enigma, and the Internet.* Cambridge, U.K.: Cambridge University Press, 2002.)

A	57	E	116	I	58	M	14	Q	3	U	25	Y	18
B	9	F	28	J	1	N	57	R	49	V	9	Z	1
C	17	G	14	K	5	O	53	S	55	W	11		
D	26	H	46	L	34	P	18	T	91	X	1		

Name _____   Date _____

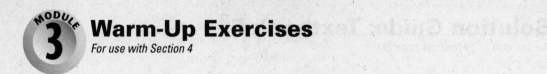

Write each fraction in lowest terms.

1. $\dfrac{4}{16}$

2. $\dfrac{14}{105}$

3. $\dfrac{4}{9}$

4. $\dfrac{4}{5} + \dfrac{1}{8}$

5. $\dfrac{7}{24} + \dfrac{1}{8}$

6. $\dfrac{1}{2} - \dfrac{1}{9}$

ANSWERS

1. $\dfrac{1}{4}$ 2. $\dfrac{2}{15}$ 3. $\dfrac{4}{9}$ 4. $\dfrac{37}{40}$ 5. $\dfrac{5}{12}$ 6. $\dfrac{7}{18}$

Name _____ Date _____

Robots Through the Maze (Use with Questions 25–27 on pages 209–210.)

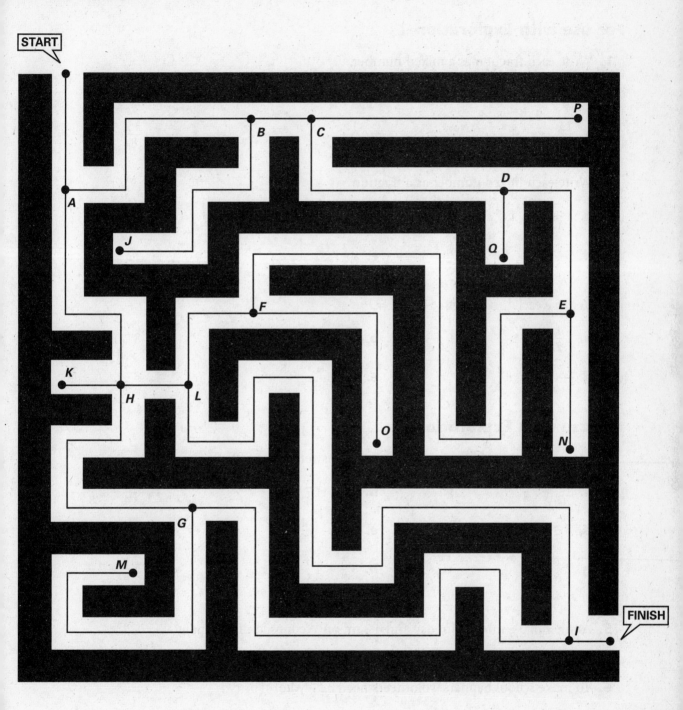

Name _____ Date _____

Practice and Applications

For use with Section 4

For use with Exploration 1

1. Write each fraction as a mixed number.

   a. $\frac{15}{4}$ **b.** $\frac{9}{5}$ **c.** $\frac{22}{6}$

   d. $\frac{13}{8}$ **e.** $\frac{11}{3}$ **f.** $\frac{35}{8}$

2. Write each mixed number as a fraction.

   a. $1\frac{7}{12}$ **b.** $2\frac{5}{6}$ **c.** $4\frac{3}{4}$

   d. $5\frac{1}{3}$ **e.** $9\frac{3}{8}$ **f.** $12\frac{4}{5}$

3. Replace each ___**?**___ with >, <, or =.

   a. $2\frac{1}{2}$ ___**?**___ $\frac{5}{3}$ **b.** $\frac{9}{8}$ ___**?**___ $1\frac{1}{8}$ **c.** 8 ___**?**___ $\frac{9}{2}$

   d. $\frac{17}{6}$ ___**?**___ $3\frac{1}{6}$ **e.** $\frac{27}{5}$ ___**?**___ $5\frac{5}{2}$ **f.** $3\frac{2}{3}$ ___**?**___ $\frac{8}{3}$

For use with Exploration 2

4. Find each sum or difference. Write each answer in lowest terms.

   a. $1\frac{2}{3} + 2\frac{1}{4}$ **b.** $3\frac{1}{5} + 4\frac{2}{3}$ **c.** $6\frac{1}{4} + 2\frac{5}{8}$

   d. $8\frac{2}{3} - 3\frac{1}{4}$ **e.** $10\frac{5}{9} - 4\frac{1}{6}$ **f.** $15\frac{1}{2} - 8\frac{3}{4}$

   g. $2\frac{1}{6} + 3\frac{2}{3}$ **h.** $3\frac{3}{8} + 4\frac{3}{4}$ **i.** $5\frac{1}{6} + 7\frac{1}{2}$

5. Annie ran $3\frac{1}{2}$ mi on Monday and $4\frac{3}{4}$ mi on Wednesday. How many more miles must Annie run if she wants to run 15 miles by Friday?

6. To make school banners, volunteers need $32\frac{5}{8}$ yd of fabric.

   a. They have $18\frac{1}{2}$ yd of fabric. How many more yards of fabric do they need?

   b. A parent donates $10\frac{2}{3}$ yd of fabric. How many more yards of fabric will the volunteers need now?

(continued)

Name _____   Date _____

MODULE 3 Practice and Applications
For use with Section 4

For use with Exploration 3

7. Draw line segments with the following lengths.

a. $1\frac{1}{2}$ in.   **b.** $4\frac{3}{4}$ in.   **c.** $3\frac{1}{4}$ in.

d. 2 in.   **e.** $5\frac{1}{4}$ in.   **f.** $2\frac{1}{2}$ in.

8. Use a ruler to measure the following line segments. Measure each length to the nearest $\frac{1}{4}$ of an inch.

a. M •————————————• N

b. O •——————————————————————————————————• P

c. Q •————————————————————————• R

d. S •——————• T

e. U •——————————————————————————————• V

f. W •————————• X

9. Replace each ___?___ with the correct measurement. Write each answer as a mixed number with the fraction in lowest terms.

a. 2 mi = ___?___ yd   **b.** 4 ft = ___?___ in.

c. $1\frac{1}{2}$ ft = ___?___ in.   **d.** 2 yd = ___?___ ft

e. 30 in. = ___?___ ft   **f.** 1 yd = ___?___ in.

g. 54 in. = ___?___ ft   **h.** 78 ft = ___?___ yd

i. 616 in. = ___?___ yd   **j.** 29 ft = ___?___ yd

k. 13,750 yd = ___?___ mi   **l.** 6600 ft = ___?___ mi

10. Assume that the average giraffe is 17 feet tall.

a. How many inches tall is the average giraffe?

b. How many yards tall is the average giraffe? State your answer to the nearest $\frac{1}{3}$ of a yard.

c. How many giraffes would have to stand on top of each other to reach a height of 51 feet?

11. The dimensions of Marta's rectangular backyard are $9\frac{1}{2}$ yd by $6\frac{3}{4}$ yd. Marta wants to build a fence for her backyard. What total length of fencing does she need

a. in yards?

b. in feet?

c. in inches?

Name _____   Date _____

Study Guide
For use with Section 4

Robot Codes   Fractions, Mixed Numbers, and Customary Length

GOAL   **LEARN HOW TO:** • write fractions as mixed numbers
• write mixed numbers as fractions
• add and subtract mixed numbers
• measure lengths using customary units
• convert between customary units of length

AS YOU: • calculate the distance traveled by a robot
• guide a robot through a maze

Exploration 1: Fractions and Mixed Numbers

A **mixed number** is the sum of a nonzero whole number and a fraction between 0 and 1. You can write a fraction as a mixed number.

Example
Write $\frac{13}{4}$ as a mixed number.

Sample Response

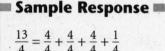

$\frac{13}{4} = \frac{4}{4} + \frac{4}{4} + \frac{4}{4} + \frac{1}{4}$

$= 1 + 1 + 1 + \frac{1}{4}$

$= 3\frac{1}{4}$ *Think*: 4 fourths make 1 whole.

You can write a mixed number as a fraction by reversing the process shown in the Example above.

Example
Write $2\frac{1}{8}$ as a fraction.

Sample Response

$2\frac{1}{8} = 1 + 1 + \frac{1}{8}$ ← *Think*: 1 whole makes 8 eighths.

$= \frac{8}{8} + \frac{8}{8} + \frac{1}{8}$

$= \frac{17}{8}$

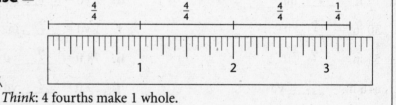

Study Guide
For use with Section 4

Exploration 2: Adding and Subtracting Mixed Numbers

You can add and subtract mixed numbers.

Example

a. Find $5\frac{2}{3} - 4\frac{1}{3}$.

b. Find $4\frac{3}{4} + 5\frac{1}{2}$.

Sample Response

a.

$$\begin{array}{r} 5\frac{2}{3} \\ -\ 4\frac{1}{3} \\ \hline 1\frac{1}{3} \end{array}$$

b.

$$\begin{array}{rll} 4\frac{3}{4} & = & 4\frac{3}{4} \\ +\ 5\frac{1}{2} & = & +\ 5\frac{2}{4} \\ \hline & & 9\frac{5}{4} = 10\frac{1}{4} \end{array}$$

← The common denominator is 4.

Mixed number subtraction problems may require regrouping, where one whole is written as a fraction whose denominator matches the denominator of the fractional part of the mixed number.

Example

Find $7\frac{1}{4} - 2\frac{5}{8}$.

Sample Response

Rewrite each fractional part using a common denominator. Then subtract, regrouping as necessary. The difference should be simplified, if possible.

$$\begin{array}{rcccl} 7\frac{1}{4} & = & 7\frac{2}{8} & = & 6\frac{10}{8} \\ -\ 2\frac{5}{8} & = & -\ 2\frac{5}{8} & = & -\ 2\frac{5}{8} \\ \hline & & & & 4\frac{5}{8} \end{array}$$

$\leftarrow 7\frac{2}{8} = 6 + \frac{8}{8} + \frac{2}{8} = 6\frac{10}{8}$

Study Guide
For use with Section 4

Exploration 3: Customary Length

The table below shows the relationship among some commonly used customary units of length.

Customary Units for Length	
inch (in.)	1 in. $= \frac{1}{12}$ ft
foot (ft)	1 ft = 12 in.
yard (yd)	1 yd = 3 ft
mile (mi)	1 mi $=$ 5280 ft $=$ 1760 yd

You can convert between different customary units of length.

Example

   a. How many inches are in 3 ft?

   b. How many feet are in 3 yd?

   c. How many yards are in 72 in.?

Sample Response

  a. 3 ft $= 3 \cdot 12$ in. ←To convert from feet to inches, multiply by 12.
         $= 36$ in.

  b. 3 yd $= 3 \cdot 3$ ft ←To convert from yards to feet, multiply by 3.
         $= 9$ ft

  c. 72 in. $= \frac{72}{12}$ ft ←To convert from inches to yards, first divide by 12 to
         $= 6$ ft   convert to feet.

     6 ft $= \frac{6}{3}$ yd ←To convert from feet to yards, divide by 3.
         $= 2$ yd

Name _____   Date _____

Study Guide: Practice & Application Exercises
For use with Section 4

Exploration 1

Write each fraction as a mixed number.

1. $\frac{37}{4}$ **2.** $\frac{41}{6}$ **3.** $\frac{29}{3}$ **4.** $\frac{125}{12}$

Write each mixed number as a fraction.

5. $2\frac{3}{4}$ **6.** $11\frac{6}{7}$ **7.** $7\frac{2}{3}$ **8.** $3\frac{3}{8}$

Exploration 2

Find each sum or difference.

9. $2\frac{1}{3} + 3\frac{5}{6}$ **10.** $12 + 1\frac{3}{4}$ **11.** $4\frac{1}{9} + 3\frac{5}{18}$

12. $14\frac{1}{2} - 9\frac{1}{3}$ **13.** $4\frac{4}{9} - 2\frac{1}{3}$ **14.** $9\frac{9}{11} - 3\frac{5}{7}$

15. $2\frac{4}{7} + 3\frac{5}{28}$ **16.** $5\frac{7}{12} - 3\frac{4}{15}$ **17.** $11\frac{5}{18} + 1\frac{3}{10}$

18. $7\frac{1}{3} - 3\frac{1}{2}$ **19.** $9\frac{3}{22} - 2\frac{5}{11}$ **20.** $\frac{3}{4} + 5\frac{7}{12}$

21. $22 - \frac{5}{18}$ **22.** $25 + \frac{3}{16}$ **23.** $4\frac{1}{10} - 2\frac{9}{25}$

24. $15\frac{1}{3} - 12\frac{3}{16}$ **25.** $4\frac{3}{8} + 9\frac{5}{24}$ **26.** $10\frac{1}{5} - 4\frac{2}{3}$

27. Algebra Connection Write an equation relating the perimeter and the lengths of the sides of the triangle. Then solve for x.

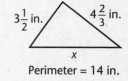

Exploration 3

Use the diagram shown at right for Exercises 28 and 29. One lap around the track in the diagram is $\frac{1}{4}$ mile.

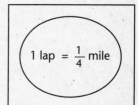

28. Determine how long one lap around the track is in the following customary units of length.

    a. feet   **b.** yards

29. How many laps would Sarah have to run around the track to have run 880 yards?

Name _____   Date _____

Quick Quiz

For use after Section 4

1. Write $\frac{63}{12}$ as a mixed number in lowest terms.

2. Write $2\frac{31}{100}$ as a fraction.

3. Find the sum $1\frac{3}{4} + 3\frac{5}{12} + 2\frac{8}{16}$.

4. Find the difference $8\frac{9}{14} - 3\frac{6}{7}$.

5. Your mother has $2\frac{3}{4}$ yd of fabric and she needs $4\frac{1}{8}$ yd to complete a project. How many more yards of fabric does she need to buy?

Name _____   Date _____

Practice and Applications

For use after Sections 1–4

For use with Section 1

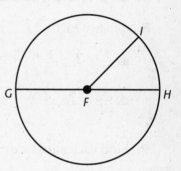

1. a. Use a ruler to measure the diameter of the circle in centimeters.

b. Use a ruler to measure radius $\overline{FI}$ in centimeters.

c. What is the circumference of the circle? Round to the nearest hundredth.

2. Use a ruler to classify each of the following triangles as *isosceles*, *equilateral*, or *scalene*.

a.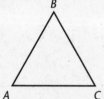

b.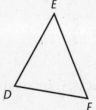

c.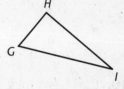

3. Use a protractor to classify each of the following triangles as *acute*, *obtuse*, or *right*.

a.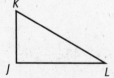

b.

c.

4. Use a compass and a ruler to construct the perpendicular bisector of $\overline{AB}$.

For use with Section 2

5. Find all the factors of each number.

a. 23   **b.** 36   **c.** 45

6. Tell whether each number is *prime* or *composite*.

a. 37   **b.** 39   **c.** 42

d. 63   **e.** 83   **f.** 95

7. Find the prime factorization of each number.

a. 42   **b.** 56   **c.** 65

(continued)

Practice and Applications
For use after Sections 1–4

For use with Section 3

8. Replace each ___?___ with >, <, or =.

a. $\frac{5}{9}$ ___?___ $\frac{5}{11}$

b. $\frac{47}{48}$ ___?___ $\frac{48}{49}$

c. $\frac{12}{25}$ ___?___ $\frac{10}{12}$

d. $\frac{24}{25}$ ___?___ $\frac{8}{9}$

e. $\frac{14}{25}$ ___?___ $\frac{14}{27}$

f. $\frac{9}{16}$ ___?___ $\frac{13}{18}$

9. Find each sum or difference. Write each answer in lowest terms.

a. $\frac{2}{3} - \frac{4}{9}$

b. $\frac{11}{12} - \frac{5}{8}$

c. $\frac{4}{15} + \frac{2}{3}$

d. $\frac{3}{8} + \frac{1}{6}$

e. $\frac{2}{3} - \frac{5}{11}$

f. $\frac{5}{12} + \frac{2}{9}$

10. Carl has a rock collection. Of the rocks, $\frac{3}{8}$ are quartz and $\frac{1}{3}$ are granite. What fraction of Carl's rocks are quartz or granite?

For use with Section 4

11. Find each sum or difference. Write each answer in lowest terms.

a. $3\frac{2}{3} + 1\frac{5}{9}$

b. $6\frac{2}{3} - 4\frac{2}{5}$

c. $48\frac{1}{3} - 26\frac{1}{2}$

d. $6\frac{3}{4} + 9\frac{5}{6}$

e. $6\frac{3}{4} - 2\frac{1}{2}$

f. $15 - 4\frac{7}{12}$

g. $78\frac{1}{2} - 24\frac{3}{4}$

h. $12\frac{1}{2} + 8\frac{7}{10}$

i. $18\frac{5}{6} - 4\frac{3}{5}$

12. Replace each ___?___ with the correct measurement. Write each answer as a mixed number with the fraction in lowest terms.

a. $2\frac{1}{2}$ yd = ___?___ in.

b. 4 ft = ___?___ in.

c. 9 in. = ___?___ ft

d. $8\frac{1}{2}$ ft = ___?___ in.

e. 9 ft = ___?___ yd

f. 18 in. = ___?___ yd

13. Replace each ___?___ with >, <, or = .

a. 5 ft ___?___ $1\frac{1}{2}$ yd

b. 16 in. ___?___ $1\frac{1}{2}$ ft

c. 4 yd ___?___ 130 in.

d. $2\frac{1}{2}$ ft ___?___ $\frac{3}{4}$ yd

e. 6 in. ___?___ $\frac{3}{4}$ ft

f. 2 yd ___?___ 72 in.

Math Thematics, Book 2
Teacher's Resource Book, Modules 3 and 4

Name _____   Date _____

Test Form A

For use after Module 3

Tell whether each set of side lengths *can* or *cannot* form a triangle. If they can, tell whether the triangle is *isosceles*, *scalene*, or *equilateral*.

1. 8 in., 5 in., 5 in.   **2.** 2 mi, 2 mi, 6 mi   **3.** 17 mm, 12 mm, 25 mm

Use 3.14 or the $\boxed{\pi}$ key on a calculator. Find the circumference of a circle with each measure. If necessary, round each answer to the nearest hundredth.

4. $r = 10$ ft   **5.** $d = 3$ in.

6. Construct a triangle with side lengths 2 in., $2\frac{1}{2}$ in., and 4 in.

7. a. Draw a segment $3\frac{5}{8}$ in. long.

   b. Construct the perpendicular bisector of the segment.

Find the prime factorization of each number using exponents.

8. 144   **9.** 65

Find the greatest common factor (GCF) of each group of numbers.

10. 10 and 15   **11.** 16, 28, and 64

Name _____ Date _____

Test Form A
For use after Module 3

Find the least common multiple (LCM) of each group of numbers.

12. 10 and 15

13. 16, 28, and 64

Write the correct symbol, >, <, or =, in each blank.

14. $\frac{2}{7}$ _____ $\frac{3}{14}$

15. $\frac{16}{24}$ _____ $\frac{20}{30}$

16. $\frac{6}{11}$ _____ $\frac{2}{3}$

17. Explain why $\frac{13}{20}$ is in lowest terms.

18. Give the measure of the item at the right

    a. to the nearest inch.

    b. to the nearest half inch.

    c. to the nearest fourth inch.

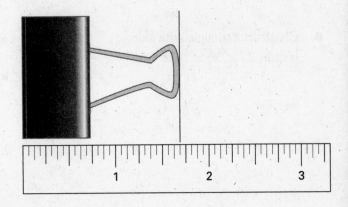

Write the correct measure in each blank.

19. 120 in. = _____ yd

20. $2\frac{3}{4}$ ft = _____ in.

If possible, rename each fraction as a mixed number.

21. $\frac{35}{4}$

22. $\frac{21}{24}$

Find each sum or difference. Write answers in lowest terms.

23. $\frac{2}{5} + \frac{9}{10}$

24. $10\frac{3}{8} - 7\frac{3}{4}$

25. $6\frac{8}{10} + 7\frac{3}{25}$

Math Thematics, Book 2
Teacher's Resource Book, Modules 3 and 4

3-48

Name _____   Date _____

Tell whether each set of side lengths *can* or *cannot* form a triangle. If they can, tell whether the triangle is *isosceles*, *scalene*, or *equilateral*.

1. 8 in., 4 in., 4 in.

2. 5 mi, 5 mi, 6 mi

3. 13 mm, 19 mm, 21 mm

Use 3.14 or the $\boxed{\pi}$ key on a calculator. Find the circumference of a circle with each measure. If necessary, round each answer to the nearest hundredth.

4. $r = 5$ ft

5. $d = 11$ in.

6. Construct a triangle with side lengths 4 in., $2\frac{1}{2}$ in., and 3 in.

7. **a.** Draw a segment $2\frac{3}{8}$ in. long.

b. Construct the perpendicular bisector of the segment.

Find the prime factorization of each number using exponents.

8. 180

9. 75

Find the greatest common factor (GCF) of each group of numbers.

10. 15 and 25

11. 14, 56, and 70

Name _____ Date _____

Test Form B
For use after Module 3

Find the least common multiple (LCM) of each group of numbers.

12. 15 and 25

13. 14, 56, and 70

Write the correct symbol, >, <, or =, in each blank.

14. $\dfrac{3}{5}$ _____ $\dfrac{11}{20}$

15. $\dfrac{7}{8}$ _____ $\dfrac{8}{9}$

16. $\dfrac{21}{28}$ _____ $\dfrac{9}{12}$

17. Explain why $\dfrac{11}{20}$ is in lowest terms.

18. Give the measure of the length of the rectangle below

   a. to the nearest inch.

   b. to the nearest half inch.

   c. to the nearest fourth inch.

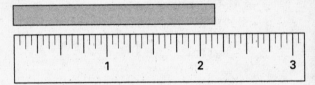

Write the correct measure in each blank.

19. 108 in. = _____ yd

20. $2\dfrac{1}{4}$ ft = _____ in.

If possible, rename each fraction as a mixed number.

21. $\dfrac{27}{4}$

22. $\dfrac{12}{15}$

Find each sum or difference. Write answers in lowest terms.

23. $\dfrac{3}{5} + \dfrac{19}{20}$

24. $8\dfrac{3}{4} - 2\dfrac{7}{8}$

25. $1\dfrac{8}{10} + 5\dfrac{2}{15}$

Math Thematics, Book 2
Teacher's Resource Book, Modules 3 and 4

Name _____   Date _____

Standardized Test
For use after Module 3

1. Which of the following is *not* a factor of 840?
   a. 14   **b.** 35
   c. 62   **d.** 84

2. Which of these numbers is prime?
   a. 21   **b.** 23
   c. 27   **d.** 84

3. Which of these numbers is divisible by 6?
   a. 1086   **b.** 4258
   c. 6003   **d.** 2026

4. What is the least common multiple of 42 and 70?
   a. 7   **b.** 112
   c. 142   **d.** 210

5. Which of the following pairs of measurements are equivalent?
   a. 8 in., 1 ft   **b.** 1 yd, $2\frac{1}{2}$ ft
   c. $1\frac{1}{2}$ ft, 18 in.   **d.** 30 in., $\frac{1}{2}$ yd

6. Which of the following sets of side lengths *cannot* form a triangle?
   a. 2 in., 9 in., 10 in.
   b. 4 ft, 4 ft, 4 ft
   c. 1 cm, 1 cm, 3 cm
   d. 16 m, 30 m, 16 m

7. Find the sum $2\frac{4}{9} + 3\frac{17}{18}$.
   a. $5\frac{7}{18}$ **b.** $5\frac{21}{27}$
   c. $6\frac{7}{18}$ **d.** $6\frac{7}{9}$

8. Which of the following line segment lengths is the shortest?
   a. $\frac{1}{2}$ ft   **b.** 8 in.
   c. $\frac{1}{4}$ yd   **d.** 10 in.

9. What is the circumference of a circle with a diameter of 8.2 in? (Use 3.14 for π and round the answer to the nearest tenth.)
   a. 12.9 in.   **b.** 25.7 in.
   c. 51.5 in.   **d.** 52.8 in.

10. Find the greatest fraction.
   a. $\frac{11}{23}$ **b.** $\frac{4}{11}$
   c. $\frac{11}{18}$ **d.** $\frac{5}{9}$

11. One lap around a track is $\frac{1}{8}$ of a mile. If you have run 1320 yd, how many laps have you run?
   a. 2   **b.** 4
   c. 6   **d.** 10

12. Refer to the figure below.

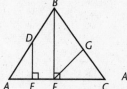

Which of the following line segments is the perpendicular bisector of $\overline{AC}$?
   a. $\overline{DE}$ **b.** $\overline{BF}$
   c. $\overline{FG}$ **d.** $\overline{AB}$

Name _____   Date _____

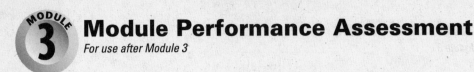

Module Performance Assessment
For use after Module 3

Meridith makes colored glass pieces that she uses to repair glass designs or to sell to other artists at craft fairs.

Step 1: Suppose she makes a set of 60 glass pieces. If she sells the pieces in packs containing an equal number of pieces, describe all the possible ways she can package the pieces.

Step 2: Each glass piece is in the shape of an equilateral triangle. Write an equation that shows the relationship between the length of one side of the triangular piece, s, with the total perimeter P. Solve the equation to find the perimeter if the length of one side is 9.5 cm.

Step 3: Use estimation to sketch a model of one of the glass pieces. Do you think it would be practical to use the piece in a jewelry design? Explain.

Step 4: A customer approaches Meridith at the booth and asks her if she can replace a damaged section of a stained glass window. The customer tells Meridith that the damaged section is in the shape of a triangle, with dimensions of $8\frac{1}{4}$ in., $4\frac{3}{8}$ in., and $12\frac{3}{4}$ in. Meridith tells the customer she must have measured the damaged section incorrectly. Explain why.

Step 5: Meridith's next project is to construct several stained glass windows that are in the shape of equilateral triangles, measuring 3 ft on each side. She can only make individual triangles that are 3 in., 5 in., or 8 in. on each side. If the window has to be made up entirely of equal-sized small triangles, which size should she use? Explain why.

Contents

Book 2	Teacher's Resources for Module 4

The Art of Motion

Name _____   Date _____

 Module Diagnostic Test
For use before Module 4

1. What is the reciprocal of $2\frac{3}{8}$?   (Sec. 1)

   A. $2\frac{8}{3}$ **B.** $-2\frac{3}{8}$ **C.** $\frac{19}{8}$ **D.** $\frac{8}{19}$

2. Find the product $\frac{2}{3} \cdot 3\frac{1}{5}$.   (Sec. 1)

   A. $\frac{32}{15}$ **B.** $3\frac{2}{15}$ **C.** $3\frac{30}{15}$ **D.** none of these

3. Find the quotient $\frac{7}{12} \div \frac{5}{6}$.   (Sec. 1)

   A. $\frac{10}{7}$ **B.** $\frac{7}{10}$ **C.** $\frac{72}{35}$ **D.** none of these

4. Which measure is a reasonable estimate for the length of a textbook?   (Sec. 2)

   A. 26.5 m   **B.** 26.5 cm   **C.** 26.5 mm   **D.** 2.65 cm

5. What measure could you write in the blank to make the statement
206 mm = _____ m true?   (Sec. 2)

   A. 206,000   **B.** 2060   **C.** 20.6   **D.** 0.206

6. Find the product of 3.9 and 0.2.   (Sec. 3)

   A. 78   **B.** 7.8   **C.** 0.78   **D.** 0.0078

7. Use estimation to determine the quotient of 3.216 ÷ 6.7.   (Sec. 3)

   A. 480   **B.** 4.8   **C.** 0.48   **D.** 0.048

8. A block of cheese weighs 42.2 ounces. How many slices that weigh 1.2 ounces can
be cut from the block?   (Sec. 3)

   A. 35   **B.** 41   **C.** 50   **D.** 351

9. Which of the following fractions can be written as a terminating decimal?   (Sec. 3)

   A. $\frac{3}{5}$ **B.** $\frac{5}{12}$ **C.** $\frac{3}{7}$ **D.** $\frac{2}{3}$

Module Diagnostic Test

For use before Module 4

10. Write the decimal $21.4\overline{73}$ carried out to six decimal places.   (Sec. 3)

   A. 21.473473   **B.** 21.473737   **C.** 21.473333   **D.** 21.473000

11. Which of the figures has rotational symmetry?   (Sec. 4)

   A.   **B.** Ⓚ   **C.** Ⓨ   **D.** Ⓧ

12. How many lines of symmetry does the figure at the right have?   (Sec. 4)

   A. 0   **B.** 1   **C.** 2   **D.** more than 2

Find each quotient or product.

13. $-24 \div -6$ **14.** $5(-8)$ **15.** $(-2)(-1)(-8)(-3)$ (Sec. 5)

16. Evaluate the expression for the given values of the variables.   (Sec. 5)

   $2m - 5p + m$ when $m = -3$ and $p = \dfrac{2}{5}$

   A. 7   **B.** -7 **C.** 11   **D.** -11

17. Which of the tranformations will move point (x, y) on a coordinate plane
5 units to the left and 2 units up?   (Sec. 6)

   A. $(2x, -5y)$ **B.** $(-5x, 2y)$ **C.** $(x + 2, y - 5)$ **D.** $(x - 5, y + 2)$

Solve each equation. Check each solution.   (Sec. 6)

18. $5x - 4 = 141$ **19.** $\dfrac{y}{3} + 7 = 19$

The Math Gazette
The Art of Motion

Sneak Preview!

Over the next several weeks, we will be exploring art that "moves" and the geometry, number, and algebra concepts on which it is based. Some of the art forms we will see are:

► optical illusions

► wind sculptures

► designs that repeat in different ways

► art from different cultures, especially Native American

► animated pictures

Ask Your Student

How are fractions and decimals used to describe the relationship between the size of an object in a photo and the actual size of the object? (Sec. 3)

What mathematics do you see in art and photography? (Sec. 3, Sec. 4, and Sec. 6)

Where can you see reflections, rotations, similar figures, and congruent figures in your daily lives? (Sec. 4 and Sec. 6)

Connections

Literature:
A popular adult author, John Jakes, has written an historical novel, *Homeland*, set in the early part of the twentieth century. The main character, a German immigrant, has an interest in photography and motion picture art, including a zoetrope. (See Module Project.)

Social Studies:
Students will learn how reflections and rotations are used in the art of various cultures. Many diverse cultures use artistic techniques that are much the same. Look for examples of this mathematics in art at your local museum or library.

E² Project

Following Section 4, students will have approximately one week to complete the Extended Exploration (E²), *Congruent Snowflakes*. Students will use their knowledge of geometric figures, reflection, and rotation to complete this project.

Students might use some of the following materials for the project:

► large sheets of plain paper

► scissors, ruler, compass, or protractor

Module Project

After completing the module, students will construct a zoetrope, one of the first moving picture machines. They will create their own moving pictures in which objects shrink, expand, and move about and show their motion pictures to the class.

The Art of Motion

Section Title	Mathematics Students Will Be Learning	Activities
1: The Illusion of Motion	◆ multiplying and dividing fractions and mixed numbers ◆ applying the distributive property	◆ create optical illusions
2: Wind Machines	◆ estimating and measuring lengths in metric units ◆ converting from one metric unit of length to another	◆ develop and use benchmarks to estimate lengths in metric units ◆ explore wind art
3: Through the Camera's Eye	◆ estimating decimal products and multiplying decimals ◆ estimating decimal quotients and dividing decimals ◆ finding repeating decimals and writing fractions as decimals	◆ play the calculator game *Hit the Target* to develop number sense about decimal products ◆ learn about motion and stop action photographs
4: The Math of Motion	◆ investigating rotations and rotational symmetry ◆ investigating reflections and line symmetry	◆ analyze transformations in artwork and in nature ◆ use a Mira® to investigate reflections
5: Special Effects	◆ multiplying and dividing integers ◆ evaluating numerical expressions that contain decimals, fractions, or integers	◆ model motion on a number line ◆ explore how larger-than-life video clips are created
6: Animation	◆ investigating translations ◆ locating translation images on a coordinate plane ◆ investigating transformations that change size and shape ◆ identifying similar figures ◆ solving two-step equations	◆ use coordinates to change the shape or location of a figure ◆ explore ways to create animations

Activities to do at Home

- Search for "optical illusions" on the internet and visit some of the sites to learn more about optical illusions and why they occur. (After Sec. 1)

- Visit a museum or borrow books on the art of various cultures from a library. Examine the art and crafts associated with your own culture. Find examples of reflections, rotations, translations, similar figures, congruent figures, and rotational and line symmetry. (After Sec. 4 and Sec. 6)

- Create a flipbook animation. (After Sec. 6)

Related Topics

You may want to discuss these related topics with your student:

 Optical illusions

 Film animation

 Native American art

 Computer graphics

Name _____   Problem _____

Teacher Assessment Scales
For use with Module 4

☆ *The star indicates that you excelled in some way.*

 Problem Solving

❶   ❷   ❸   ❹   ❺   ☆ →

❶ You did not understand the problem well enough to get started or you did not show any work.

❸ You understood the problem well enough to make a plan and to work toward a solution.

❺ You made a plan, you used it to solve the problem, and you verified your solution.

 Mathematical Language

❶   ❷   ❸   ❹   ❺   ☆ →

❶ You did not use any mathematical vocabulary or symbols, or you did not use them correctly, or your use was not appropriate.

❸ You used appropriate mathematical language, but the way it was used was not always correct or other terms and symbols were needed.

❺ You used mathematical language that was correct and appropriate to make your meaning clear.

 Representations

❶   ❷   ❸   ❹   ❺   ☆ →

❶ You did not use any representations such as equations, tables, graphs, or diagrams to help solve the problem or explain your solution.

❸ You made appropriate representations to help solve the problem or help you explain your solution, but they were not always correct or other representations were needed.

❺ You used appropriate and correct representations to solve the problem or explain your solution.

 Connections

❶   ❷   ❸   ❹   ❺   ☆ →

❶ You attempted or solved the problem and then stopped.

❸ You found patterns and used them to extend the solution to other cases, or you recognized that this problem relates to other problems, mathematical ideas, or applications.

❺ You extended the ideas in the solution to the general case, or you showed how this problem relates to other problems, mathematical ideas, or applications.

 Presentation

❶   ❷   ❸   ❹   ❺   ☆ →

❶ The presentation of your solution and reasoning is unclear to others.

❸ The presentation of your solution and reasoning is clear in most places, but others may have trouble understanding parts of it.

❺ The presentation of your solution and reasoning is clear and can be understood by others.

Content Used: _____   **Computational Errors:** Yes ☐ No ☐

Notes on Errors: _____

_____

Math Thematics, Book 2
Teacher's Resource Book, Modules 3 and 4

Name _____   Problem _____

MODULE 4

Student Self-Assessment Scales

For use with Module 4

▭ If your score is in the shaded area, explain why on the back of this sheet and stop.

☆ The star indicates that you excelled in some way.

Problem Solving

❶ I did not understand the problem well enough to get started or I did not show any work.

❷ I understood the problem well enough to make a plan and to work toward a solution.

❸ I made a plan, I used it to solve the problem, and I verified my solution.

Mathematical Language

❶ I did not use any mathematical vocabulary or symbols, or I did not use them correctly, or my use was not appropriate.

❸ I used appropriate mathematical language, but the way it was used was not always correct or other terms and symbols were needed.

❺ I used mathematical language that was correct and appropriate to make my meaning clear.

Representations

❶ I did not use any representations such as equations, tables, graphs, or diagrams to help solve the problem or explain my solution.

❸ I made appropriate representations to help solve the problem or help me explain my solution, but they were not always correct or other representations were needed.

❺ I used appropriate and correct representations to solve the problem or explain my solution.

Connections

❶ I attempted or solved the problem and then stopped.

❸ I found patterns and used them to extend the solution to other cases, or I recognized that this problem relates to other problems, mathematical ideas, or applications.

❺ I extended the ideas in the solution to the general case, or I showed how this problem relates to other problems, mathematical ideas, or applications.

Presentation

❶ The presentation of my solution and reasoning is unclear to others.

❸ The presentation of my solution and reasoning is clear in most places, but others may have trouble understanding parts of it.

❺ The presentation of my solution and reasoning is clear and can be understood by others.

Warm-Up Exercises

For use with Section 1

Rewrite each mixed or whole number as a fraction.

1. $1\frac{2}{3}$

2. 6

3. $5\frac{4}{9}$

Which of the following measurements on a ruler is greater?

4. $\frac{1}{2}$ in. or $\frac{3}{8}$ in.

5. $1\frac{5}{16}$ in. or $1\frac{1}{4}$ in.

6. $\frac{7}{8}$ in. or $\frac{15}{16}$ in.

ANSWERS

1. $\frac{5}{3}$ 2. $\frac{6}{1}$ 3. $\frac{49}{9}$ 4. $\frac{1}{2}$ in.   5. $1\frac{5}{16}$ in.   6. $\frac{15}{16}$ in.

The Café Wall (Use with Questions 3 and 4 on page 227 and Questions 7 and 8 on page 228.)

Directions Cut out the strips at the bottom of the page by cutting along the gray lines. Then follow the directions in your book to complete the Café Wall illusion.

MODULE 4   **LABSHEET** **1B**

The Bull's-eye Illusion (Use with Questions 23 and 24 on page 231.)

Directions

- The radius of Circle 1, the circle at the center of the Bull's-eye, is $\frac{1}{4}$ in.

- For Circles 2–6, the radius of each circle is the radius of the previous circle divided by the fraction shown in the table. Complete the table.

- Use a compass to draw Circles 2–6. The center of each circle is at point O. Use the ruler below to adjust the radius of your compass to the correct measure.

Circle	Radius (in.)
Circle 1	$\frac{1}{4}$
Circle 2	$\frac{1}{4} \div \frac{1}{2} =$ _____
Circle 3	_____ $\div \frac{2}{3} =$ _____
Circle 4	_____ $\div \frac{3}{4} =$ _____
Circle 5	_____ $\div \frac{4}{5} =$ _____
Circle 6	_____ $\div \frac{5}{6} =$ _____

The Bull's-eye Illusion

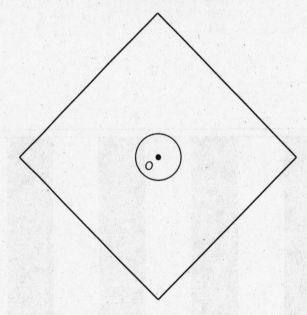

Name _____ Date _____

For use with Exploration 1

1. Find each product. Write each answer in lowest terms.

a. $\frac{2}{5} \cdot \frac{1}{4}$ **b.** $\frac{4}{5} \cdot \frac{5}{12}$ **c.** $\frac{2}{3} \cdot \frac{9}{10}$

d. $\frac{3}{4} \cdot \frac{5}{6}$ **e.** $\frac{1}{2} \cdot \frac{8}{9}$ **f.** $\frac{1}{8} \cdot \frac{1}{5}$

g. $2\frac{1}{3} \cdot 4\frac{1}{2}$ **h.** $3\frac{1}{4} \cdot 2\frac{2}{5}$ **i.** $3\frac{1}{4} \cdot 4\frac{3}{8}$

j. $\frac{3}{8} \cdot \frac{4}{5}$ **k.** $\frac{10}{20} \cdot \frac{6}{8}$ **l.** $\frac{1}{10} \cdot \frac{2}{3}$

m. $\frac{16}{25} \cdot \frac{5}{12}$ **n.** $\frac{7}{8} \cdot \frac{16}{21}$ **o.** $\frac{2}{3} \cdot \frac{4}{9} \cdot \frac{3}{8}$

2. Calvin has $2\frac{5}{6}$ yd of fabric. He uses $\frac{3}{8}$ of the fabric to make a kite.

How much of the fabric does Calvin use to make the kite?

3. Emily has $2\frac{1}{2}$ lb of spinach. She needs $\frac{1}{7}$ of the spinach for a recipe.

How much spinach does she need?

4. Find the reciprocal of each number.

a. $\frac{1}{5}$ **b.** $2\frac{1}{6}$ **c.** 27

d. $\frac{6}{7}$ **e.** $3\frac{3}{5}$ **f.** $\frac{5}{6}$

g. $\frac{17}{6}$ **h.** $4\frac{2}{3}$ **i.** 8

j. $\frac{2}{9}$ **k.** $1\frac{1}{7}$ **l.** 13

m. $6\frac{1}{3}$ **n.** $2\frac{1}{4}$ **o.** $\frac{5}{11}$

(continued)

Practice and Applications

For use with Section 1

For use with Exploration 2

5. Find each quotient. Write each answer in lowest terms.

a. $\frac{3}{4} \div \frac{3}{8}$ **b.** $\frac{18}{5} \div \frac{3}{8}$ **c.** $\frac{5}{12} \div \frac{3}{4}$

d. $2\frac{1}{5} \div \frac{1}{5}$ **e.** $2\frac{3}{4} \div \frac{1}{3}$ **f.** $5\frac{2}{3} \div 1\frac{3}{5}$

g. $4\frac{2}{7} \div 2$ **h.** $3\frac{1}{4} \div 1\frac{1}{2}$ **i.** $8 \div \frac{4}{5}$

j. $6\frac{1}{2} \div 1\frac{3}{4}$ **k.** $16 \div \frac{8}{9}$ **l.** $4\frac{2}{3} \div 2\frac{1}{3}$

m. $4 \div \frac{7}{4}$ **n.** $8 \div \frac{3}{2}$ **o.** $2 \div \frac{3}{4}$

p. $8\frac{1}{2} \div \frac{5}{8}$ **q.** $6 \div 3\frac{3}{4}$ **r.** $2\frac{1}{3} \div 1\frac{1}{2}$

s. $3\frac{1}{5} \div 2\frac{1}{4}$ **t.** $4 \div \frac{2}{5}$ **u.** $4 \div \frac{3}{4}$

6. Paul has a 15 ft long piece of rope. He wants to cut the rope into sections that are $3\frac{3}{4}$ ft long.

     a. How many $3\frac{3}{4}$ ft long pieces of rope can Paul make?

     b. Will there be any rope left over? If so, how much?

7. A sculptor has $15\frac{3}{8}$ lb of clay. She divides the clay into $1\frac{1}{2}$ lb pieces to use for models.

     a. How many pieces of clay does the sculptor have?

     b. Is there any clay left over? If so, how much?

8. A baker at the Delicious Breadbasket Bakery uses $3\frac{2}{3}$ c flour for each small loaf of French bread that he makes. He uses $4\frac{3}{4}$ c flour for every large loaf of French bread he makes. He always makes the same number of small and large loaves of French bread.

     a. How much flour does he use for one small loaf and one large loaf?

     b. How much flour will he need to make a total of 12 loaves of French bread?

Name _____   Date _____

Study Guide
For use with Section 1

The Illusion of Motion — Multiplication and Division of Fractions

GOAL **LEARN HOW TO:** • multiply fractions and mixed numbers
 • use the distributive property
 • find reciprocals
 • divide fractions and mixed numbers

AS YOU: • create an optical illusion

Exploration 1: Multiplying Fractions

To multiply fractions, you first multiply the numerators. Then you multiply the denominators.

Example
Find $\frac{1}{8} \cdot \frac{3}{5}$ in lowest terms.

Sample Response
$\frac{1}{8} \cdot \frac{3}{5} = \frac{1 \cdot 3}{5 \cdot 8} = \frac{3}{40}$

Sometimes it is easier to divide by the common factors before multiplying.

Example
Find $\frac{3}{25} \cdot \frac{20}{33}$ in lowest terms.

Sample Response
$\dfrac{3}{25} \cdot \dfrac{20}{33} = \dfrac{\overset{1}{\cancel{3}}}{\underset{5}{\cancel{25}}} \cdot \dfrac{\overset{4}{\cancel{20}}}{\underset{11}{\cancel{33}}}$ ← There are common factors of 3 and 5.
$= \dfrac{1 \cdot 4}{5 \cdot 11} = \dfrac{4}{55}$

Study Guide
For use with Section 1

You can use the distributive property to multiply a fraction and a mixed number.

Example

Find $\frac{3}{7} \cdot 2\frac{1}{4}$ in lowest terms.

Sample Response

$\frac{3}{7} \cdot 2\frac{1}{4} = \frac{3}{7}\left(2 + \frac{1}{4}\right) = \left(\frac{3}{7} \cdot 2\right) + \left(\frac{3}{7} \cdot \frac{1}{4}\right)$ ← Use the distributive property.

$= \frac{6}{7} + \frac{3}{28} = \frac{24}{28} + \frac{3}{28} = \frac{27}{28}$

Reciprocals

Two numbers whose product is 1, such as $\frac{3}{4}$ and $\frac{4}{3}$, are **reciprocals**.

Exploration 2: Dividing Fractions

To divide a number by a fraction, you multiply the number by the reciprocal of the fraction.

Example

Find $\frac{2}{5} \div \frac{3}{4}$ in lowest terms.

Sample Response

$\frac{2}{5} \div \frac{3}{4} = \frac{2}{5} \cdot \frac{4}{3} = \frac{8}{15}$

To divide mixed numbers, first express them as improper fractions.

Example

Find $1\frac{2}{3} \div \frac{5}{7}$ in lowest terms.

Sample Response

$1\frac{2}{3} \div \frac{5}{7} = \frac{5}{3} \div \frac{5}{7} = \frac{5}{3} \cdot \frac{7}{5} = \frac{\overset{1}{\cancel{5}}}{3} \cdot \frac{7}{\underset{1}{\cancel{5}}} = \frac{1 \cdot 7}{3 \cdot 1} = \frac{7}{3}, \text{ or } 2\frac{1}{3}$

Name _____   Date _____

Study Guide: Practice & Application Exercises
For use with Section 1

Exploration 1

Find each product. Write each answer in lowest terms.

1. $\frac{4}{7} \cdot \frac{1}{9}$

2. $\frac{5}{6} \cdot 3$

3. $\frac{6}{14} \cdot \frac{7}{48}$

4. $7 \cdot 3\frac{2}{7}$

5. $2\frac{4}{5} \cdot \frac{10}{28}$

6. $1\frac{1}{2} \cdot 3\frac{4}{6}$

7. $\frac{2}{3} \cdot \frac{5}{12}$

8. $1\frac{6}{13} \cdot \frac{2}{5}$

9. $8 \cdot \frac{4}{11}$

Find the reciprocal of each number.

10. 8

11. $\frac{2}{3}$

12. $\frac{5}{8}$

13. $\frac{23}{5}$

14. $5\frac{4}{9}$

15. $\frac{7}{48}$

16. 21

17. $7\frac{1}{8}$

18. $3\frac{1}{5}$

19. $\frac{7}{3}$

20. $2\frac{1}{16}$

21. $\frac{2}{9}$

22. $\frac{5}{8}$

23. $\frac{1}{38}$

24. $\frac{15}{4}$

Exploration 2

Find each quotient. Write each answer in lowest terms.

25. $\frac{4}{9} \div \frac{2}{3}$

26. $3 \div \frac{1}{5}$

27. $\frac{3}{7} \div \frac{3}{7}$

28. $\frac{1}{2} \div 1\frac{1}{2}$

29. $\frac{7}{9} \div \frac{14}{27}$

30. $3\frac{2}{3} \div \frac{6}{7}$

31. $1\frac{1}{2} \div 1\frac{4}{5}$

32. $3\frac{1}{9} \div 32$

33. $1\frac{3}{7} \div \frac{1}{11}$

34. $5\frac{1}{2} \div 2\frac{1}{4}$

35. $6 \div \frac{3}{8}$

36. $\frac{1}{4} \div 1\frac{1}{5}$

Name _____   Date _____

1. Find $\frac{4}{5} \cdot \frac{25}{80}$ in lowest terms.

2. Use the distributive property to evaluate $\frac{1}{4} \cdot 32\frac{16}{17}$.

3. Find the reciprocal of each number.

   a. $\frac{6}{5}$ **b.** $2\frac{3}{5}$ **c.** 17

4. Find $2\frac{4}{7} \div \frac{12}{21}$ in lowest terms.

5. Give an example of two fractions whose

   a. product equals 1.   **b.** quotient equals 1.

Name _____ Date _____

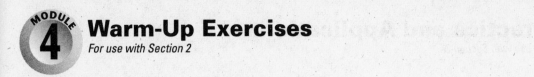

Warm-Up Exercises
MODULE 4
For use with Section 2

Write each power in standard form.

1. 10^4

2. 10^{-2}

3. 10^1

Write each number using powers of ten.

4. 0.0001

5. 10,000,000

6. 1

ANSWERS

1. 10,000 2. 0.01 3. 10 4. 10^{-4} 5. 10^7 6. 10^0

Name _____   Date _____

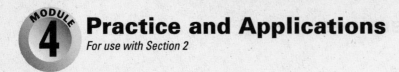

For use with Exploration 1

1. Use benchmarks to estimate and draw a segment with each length. Then check your estimates with a metric ruler.

   a. 5 cm   **b.** 80 mm   **c.** 0.3 m

2. Copy each measure. Then place a decimal point in the number so that the measure is reasonable.

   a. thickness of a ruler: 200 mm

   b. height of a desk: 60 m

   c. length of a pencil: 1370 cm

   d. length of a car: 85 m

For use with Exploration 2

3. Replace each ___?___ with the correct measure.

   a. 400 cm = ___?___ m   **b.** 36 km = ___?___ m

   c. 9.21 cm = ___?___ mm   **d.** 900 m = ___?___ km

   e. 1.8 km = ___?___ cm   **f.** 27.8 mm = ___?___ m

   g. 7.1 cm = ___?___ km   **h.** 600 km = ___?___ mm

   i. 763 m = ___?___ cm   **j.** 256 mm = ___?___ cm

4. Replace each ___?___ with >, <, or =.

   a. 0.056 km ___?___ 5.6 m   **b.** 3120 mm ___?___ 3.12 m

   c. 9 cm ___?___ 12 mm   **d.** 19.6 cm ___?___ 18.1 m

   e. 7.01 cm ___?___ 10 km   **f.** 6.2 mm ___?___ 62 km

   g. 86 mm ___?___ 25 cm   **h.** 5.6 km ___?___ 5600 mm

5. Todd jumped 0.0015 km in a long jump. How many meters did Todd jump? How many centimeters?

Name _____   Date _____

Study Guide
For use with Section 2

Wind Machines   Metric Units of Length

GOAL   **LEARN HOW TO:** • develop metric benchmarks
• use benchmarks to estimate lengths in metric units
• measure in metric units
• convert from one metric unit to another

AS YOU: • estimate and measure lengths of wind machines
• look at a wind farm

Exploration 1: Metric Length Benchmarks

Benchmarks

A **benchmark** is a number or an object that can be used as a reference. The best benchmarks are ones that can be easily and conveniently used in a variety of situations.

In the metric system, the most commonly used units of length are *millimeters*, *centimeters*, *meters*, and *kilometers*. (See page 4-20.)

        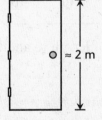   

The thickness of a dime is about 1 mm.

The diameter of a penny is about 2 cm.

The height of a door is about 2 m.

Three laps around a football field is a distance of about 1 km.

You can use something whose measure you know as a benchmark to estimate metric lengths.

Example

To estimate the length in centimeters of the segment below, use a penny as a benchmark.

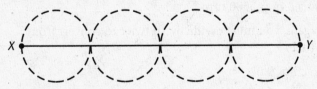

The length of the segment is about the same as the combined diameters of 4 pennies aligned in a row (8 cm).

Name _____ Date _____

 **Study Guide**
For use with Section 2

Exploration 2: Metric Conversions

Metric System

Metric measures of length are based on the *meter (m)*. The most commonly used metric units of length are related as follows:

1 **meter (m)** = 0.001 km = 100 cm = 1000 mm
1 **centimeter (cm)** = 0.01 m = 10 mm
1 **millimeter (mm)** = 0.001 m = 0.1 cm
1 **kilometer (km)** = 1000 m   ← A kilometer is used to measure long distances.

Converting Metric Units

This conversion chart shows the relationship between metric units of length.

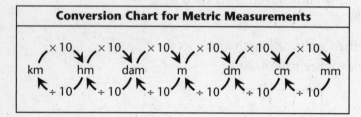

You change from one metric unit of length to another by multiplying or dividing by a power of 10.

Example

Replace each ___?___ with the correct measure.

a. 5.3 m = ___?___ mm

b. 2.6 cm = ___?___ m

Sample Response

a. Using the conversion chart above, you must multiply by 10 three times to convert from meters (m) to millimeters (mm).

$5.3 \times 10 \times 10 \times 10 = 5300$, so 5.3 m = 5300 mm

b. Using the conversion chart again, you must divide by 10 twice to convert from centimeters (cm) to meters (m).

$2.6 \div 10 \div 10 = 0.026$, so 2.6 cm = 0.026 m

Math Thematics, Book 2
Teacher's Resource Book, Modules 3 and 4

Name _____ Date _____

Exploration 1

1. Choose the most reasonable measure for the height of a house.

A. 6 mm   **B.** 6 cm   **C.** 6 m   **D.** 6 km

2. Choose the most reasonable measure for the length of a table.

A. 150 cm   **B.** 150 mm   **C.** 150 m

3. Choose the most reasonable measure for the width of a door.

A. 1 mm   **B.** 1 cm   **C.** 1 m

4. Choose the most reasonable measure for the distance from floor to ceiling.

A. 3 cm   **B.** 3 m   **C.** 3 km

5. Choose the most reasonable measure for the length of a ladybug.

A. 5 mm   **B.** 5 cm   **C.** 5 m

Exploration 2

Replace each __?__ with the correct measure.

6. 315 m = __?__ cm   **7.** 2.3 km = __?__ m

8. 8.112 cm = __?__ mm   **9.** 0.07 m = __?__ km

10. 1256 mm = __?__ km   **11.** 7.01 mm = __?__ cm

12. 6.2 km = __?__ m   **13.** 506 cm = __?__ km

14. 0.15 km = __?__ mm   **15.** 306 mm = __?__ km

Replace each __?__ with >, <, or =.

16. 7.7 m __?__ 77 cm   **17.** 0.17 km __?__ 170,000 cm

18. 3.1 m __?__ 310 km   **19.** 5.4 cm __?__ 54 mm

20. 8.9 cm __?__ 890 m   **21.** 16.7 mm __?__ 0.0167 m

22. On Saturday, Merrie ran a 5 km race. On Sunday, she ran a 1600 m race. In all, how far did Merrie run

   a. in kilometers?

   b. in meters?

Quick Quiz

For use after Section 2

1. Convert 0.82 km to cm.

2. Is 420 cm *greater than, less than,* or *equal to* 42 mm?

3. A windmill tower is 70,000 mm tall and its base is 0.008 km wide.
    Change the metric units and measures to ones that give you a better idea
    of the size of the tower.

4. The center for a women's basketball team is 214 m tall. Place the decimal
    point in 214 m so that the measure is reasonable.

5. Is it reasonable to estimate the height of a school bus as 8 m? Explain.

Name _____   Date _____

Warm-Up Exercises

For use with Section 3

Multiply.

1. $9.3875 \cdot 100$

2. $0.053 \cdot 100$

3. $193 \cdot 10$

Divide.

4. $8375.6 \div 100$

5. $138.32 \div 1000$

6. $0.3193 \div 10$

ANSWERS

1. 938.75   2. 5.3   3. 1930   4. 83.756   5. 0.13832   6. 0.03193

Math Thematics, Book 2

Name _____ Date _____

MODULE 4 Practice and Applications
For use with Section 3

For use with Exploration 1

1. Copy each problem. Use estimation to place the decimal point in each product.

   a. $(0.18)(6.1) = 1098$ b. $(318.7)(0.09) = 28683$

   c. $(5.91)(0.328) = 193848$ d. $(612.3)(2.85) = 1745055$

2. Find each product. Show your work.

   a. $(26.3)(5.32)$ b. $(0.07)(2.7)$ c. $(108.6)(0.6)$

   d. $(218.5)(0.73)$ e. $(42.15)(0.029)$ f. $(0.34)(0.47)$

   g. $(8.6)(1.93)$ h. $(1.03)(0.05)$ i. $(4.62)(0.73)$

3. Predict whether each product will be *greater than*, *less than*, or *equal to* the boldface number. Explain how you know.

   a. $(\mathbf{29.7})(0.46)$ b. $(1.59)(\mathbf{359.4})$ c. $(\mathbf{463.8})(1)$

4. Asparagus costs $3.49 per pound and snow peas cost $1.89 per pound at the market. Caitlin buys 1.8 lb of asparagus and 2.45 lb of snow peas. How much do the asparagus and snow peas cost altogether?

For use with Exploration 2

5. Copy each problem. Use estimation to place the decimal point in each quotient.

   a. $28.5 \div 0.04 = 7125$ b. $92.8 \div 6.4 = 145$

   c. $136 \div 3.2 = 425$ d. $61.2 \div 2.4 = 255$

6. Find each quotient. Show your work.

   a. $28 \div 3.5$ b. $0.45 \div 0.06$ c. $21\overline{)9.03}$

   d. $4.32 \div 0.6$ e. $0.003\overline{)42}$ f. $5.04 \div 1.4$

   g. $2.16 \div 0.4$ h. $0.34 \div 0.05$ i. $7.15 \div 2.2$

7. A circular track has a circumference of 188.4 m. What is the diameter of the track? Use 3.14 for π.

(continued)

Name _____   Date _____

Practice and Applications

For use with Section 3

For use with Exploration 3

8. Write each decimal carried out to six decimal places.

   a. $0.2\overline{69}$ **b.** $4.\overline{71}$ **c.** $0.04\overline{3}$

   d. $21.5\overline{3}$ **e.** $1.\overline{04}$ **f.** $6.1\overline{8}$

   g. $3.\overline{102}$ **h.** $123.6\overline{5}$ **i.** $4.12\overline{7}$

   j. $19.\overline{2}$ **k.** $1.7\overline{62}$ **l.** $1.\overline{809}$

9. Find each quotient. Show your work.

   a. $0.58 \div 0.6$ **b.** $0.45\overline{)14.8}$ **c.** $1.6 \div 2.7$

   d. $\dfrac{1.4}{9}$ **e.** $62.73 \div 0$ **f.** $0.11\overline{)83.5}$

   g. $0 \div 0.384$ **h.** $4.3 \div 0.9$ **i.** $25.4 \div 0.22$

10. Write each fraction as a decimal rounded to the nearest hundredth.

   a. $\dfrac{3}{8}$ **b.** $\dfrac{1}{6}$ **c.** $\dfrac{7}{9}$

   d. $\dfrac{4}{7}$ **e.** $\dfrac{2}{9}$ **f.** $\dfrac{5}{12}$

   g. $\dfrac{1}{3}$ **h.** $\dfrac{3}{11}$ **i.** $\dfrac{5}{6}$

   j. $\dfrac{6}{11}$ **k.** $\dfrac{5}{7}$ **l.** $\dfrac{7}{8}$

   m. $\dfrac{11}{12}$ **n.** $\dfrac{4}{9}$ **o.** $\dfrac{8}{11}$

11. Predict whether each quotient will be *greater than*, *less than*, or *equal to* the boldface number. Explain how you know.

   a. $\mathbf{32.56} \div 0.29$ **b.** $174\overline{)\mathbf{69.28}}$ **c.** $\mathbf{418.2} \div 1$

   d. $\mathbf{82.17} \div 0.92$ **e.** $\mathbf{436} \div 2163$ **f.** $\mathbf{53} \div 53.4$

   g. $\mathbf{289} \div 0.5$ **h.** $\mathbf{0.428} \div 6$ **i.** $\mathbf{327} \div 1.9$

12. Photographs taken for the student yearbook are 4.5 cm high. The photographs must be 1.2 cm high to fit in their spaces in the yearbook. What reduction is needed to make the photographs fit perfectly into the spaces in the yearbook?

Name _____ Date _____

Study Guide
For use with Section 3

Through the Camera's Eye   Decimal Multiplication and Division

GOAL **LEARN HOW TO:** • estimate decimal products and quotients
• multiply and divide decimals
• find quotients that repeat
• write a fraction as a decimal
• interpret division with zero

AS YOU: • examine and analyze photographs
• investigate the flight of a golf ball

Exploration 1: The Eye of the Beholder

Multiplying Decimals

To multiply decimal numbers, you first multiply them as whole numbers.
Then the number of decimal places in the product is the sum of the
number of decimal places in the factors.

> **Example**
>
> Find the product (23.1)(0.34).
>
> ```
>    23.1    ←   1 decimal place
>  × 0.34    ← + 2 decimal places
>     924         3 decimal places
>   6 930
>   7.854
> ```

Exploration 2: Keep Your Eye on the Ball

Dividing Decimals

To divide decimal numbers, you first multiply the divisor and the dividend
by a power of 10 that will make the divisor a whole number. Write zeros at
the end of the dividend as needed. Then you divide.

> **Example**
>
> Find the quotient 4.2 ÷ 0.56.
>
> ```
>           7.5
>     56) 420.0    ← Insert two zeros to
>         392         continue the division.
>         28 0
>         28 0
>            0
> ```

Name _____   Date _____

Study Guide
For use with Section 3

Exploration 3: In the Mind's Eye

Repeating and Terminating Decimals

A decimal in which a digit or a sequence of digits keeps repeating is a **repeating decimal**. A bar is written over the digits that repeat.

repeating decimal:
$1.236363636\ldots = 1.2\overline{36}$

A decimal that stops is a **terminating decimal**.

terminating decimal: 1.267

You can write the decimal equivalent of a fraction by dividing the numerator by the denominator.

> ### Example
>
> Write $\frac{4}{5}$ and $\frac{2}{3}$ as decimals.
>
> ### ▪ Sample Response ▪
>
> $\frac{4}{5} = 4 \div 5 = 0.8$ ← terminating decimal
>
> $\frac{2}{3} = 2 \div 3 = 0.666\ldots$ or $0.\overline{6}$ ← repeating decimal

When finding $4 \div 5$ using long division, there is no remainder. When finding $2 \div 3$ using long division however, the difference at each stage of the division is the same, 2, as shown at the right. For repeating decimals, this occurs at some point in the long division.

$$
\begin{array}{r}
0.66 \\
3)\overline{2.00} \\
\underline{1\,8} \\
20 \quad \leftarrow \text{difference: 2} \\
\underline{18} \\
2 \quad \leftarrow \text{difference: 2}
\end{array}
$$

Division with Zero

Zero divided by any non-zero number is always zero, because the product of zero and any non-zero number is always zero.

> ### Example
>
> $0 \div 8 = 0$, because $0 \cdot 8 = 0$.

Division by zero is undefined, because there is no unique number by which you can multiply zero to produce a non-zero product.

Name _____   Date _____

 Study Guide: Practice & Application Exercises
For use with Section 3

Exploration 1

Find each product. Show your work.

1. $(0.049)(3.4)$ **2.** $(23)(2.6)$ **3.** $(7.12)(0.84)$

4. $(0.28)(0.16)$ **5.** $(425.1)(3.7)$ **6.** $(0.73)(0.08)$

7. $(99)(25.61)$ **8.** $(1.03)(2.005)$ **9.** $(0.021)(7.8)$

10. $(12)(1.9)$ **11.** $(6.14)(0.13)$ **12.** $(0.31)(0.76)$

13. $(127.5)(2.6)$ **14.** $(0.84)(0.06)$ **15.** $(57)(45.11)$

16. Deena is buying 2.6 lb of apples. If the apples cost $1.78 per pound, how much money will Deena pay? Round your answer to the nearest cent.

Exploration 2

Find each quotient. Show your work.

17. $38 \div 2.5$ **18.** $0.16 \div 0.05$ **19.** $21.28 \div 5.6$

20. $2.52 \div 0.4$ **21.** $84 \div 0.0007$ **22.** $3.038 \div 3.1$

23. $15 \div 1.5$ **24.** $0.11 \div 0.0001$ **25.** $12.82 \div 0.2$

26. $3.27 \div 0.3$ **27.** $46 \div 2.3$ **28.** $5.075 \div 0.25$

Exploration 3

Find each quotient. Show your work.

29. $1.5 \div 0.9$ **30.** $2.8 \div 0.54$ **31.** $98.7 \div 0$

32. $3.2 \div 9$ **33.** $0 \div 57.16$ **34.** $33.75 \div 0.22$

Write each fraction as a decimal rounded to the nearest hundredth.

35. $\frac{6}{7}$ **36.** $\frac{4}{9}$ **37.** $\frac{5}{12}$

38. $\frac{1}{9}$ **39.** $\frac{3}{8}$ **40.** $\frac{3}{11}$

41. $\frac{1}{6}$ **42.** $\frac{4}{13}$ **43.** $\frac{7}{8}$

Math Thematics, Book 2

Name _____   Date _____

Quick Quiz
For use after Section 3

1. Use estimation to place the decimal in the product below.

$$(0.087)(12,345) = 1074015$$

2. Find the product $(38.4)(0.42)$.

3. Find the quotient $892.4 \div 0.6$.

4. Write $\dfrac{4}{11}$ as a decimal. Is it *repeating* or *terminating*?

5. **a.** Estimate $(0.21)(426.3)$. Describe your strategy.

b. Is your estimate *greater than* or *less than* the actual answer?

c. Find the actual answer.

Name _____ Date _____

Mid-Module Quiz

For use after Section 3

Use the distributive property to find each product.

1. $7 \cdot 5\frac{3}{14}$

2. $\frac{1}{4} \cdot 56\frac{8}{9}$

Find the reciprocal of each number.

3. $\frac{6}{7}$

4. $2\frac{3}{8}$

Find the product or quotient. Write each answer in lowest terms.

5. $\frac{2}{5} \cdot \frac{10}{11}$

6. $6\frac{2}{3} \cdot \frac{4}{5}$

7. $\frac{7}{8} \div \frac{6}{5}$

8. $1\frac{1}{7} \div 1\frac{1}{5}$

Measure the line segment below to the nearest tenth of a centimeter.

9. _____

10. Which of the following is a reasonable benchmark for 15 cm?

    A. length of a pencil   **B.** thickness of a paperclip

    C. length of an adult shoe   **D.** length of your arm from shoulder to wrist

Replace each blank with the correct measure.

11. 2.6 km = _____ m

12. 345 mm = _____ cm

Estimate each product or quotient.

13. $101.4 \div 0.094$

14. $(38.47)(0.021)$

Find each product or quotient.

15. $12.8 \div 0.02$

16. $(0.3)(2.05)$

17. $0.4 \div 6$

18. $(11.11)(0.07)$

Write each decimal carried out to seven places.

19. $0.64\overline{9}$

20. $0.3\overline{14}$

Name _____   Date _____

1. How many degrees are in a circle?

2. How many degrees are in a right angle?

3. How many degrees are in a straight angle?

4. Which figure below is the same size and shape as the given figure?

A.    **B.** 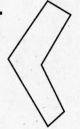   **C.**

ANSWERS

1. 360°   2. 90°   3. 180°   4. A

Stick Figure (Use with Question 3 on page 267.)

Directions

a. Draw a segment from point *Y* on Stick Figure 1 to point *P*. Draw another segment from point *Z* on Stick Figure 2 to point *P*.

b. Trace Stick Figure 1 and point *P* on tracing paper.

c. Place your tracing of Stick Figure 1 and point *P* so it fits exactly on the original.

d. Place the tip of your pencil on point *P* to keep it from moving. Then rotate your tracing paper clockwise until Stick Figure 1 fits exactly on Stick Figure 2.

e. How many degrees did you have to rotate Stick Figure 1 to match with Stick Figure 2? Explain how you found out.

f. Repeat parts (c)–(e), but this time rotate counterclockwise.

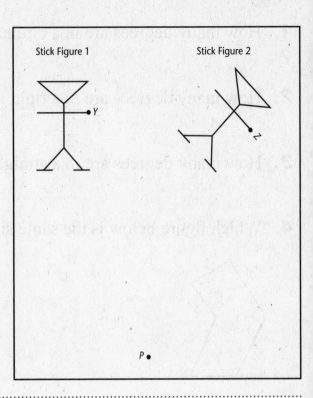

Six-Pointed Star (Use with Questions 7 and 8 on page 268.)

Directions

a. Trace the star and point *P* on tracing paper. Be sure to include the labels.

b. Place your tracing of the star so that it fits exactly on the original star. Then place the tip of your pencil on point *P* and slowly rotate the tracing clockwise until point *A* on the tracing reaches point *B* on the original star.

c. Does the rotated star fit exactly on itself?

d. Continue rotating the tracing of the star clockwise around point *P* until point *A* on the tracing reaches points *C*, *D*, *E*, *F*, and, finally, *A* on the original star.

e. How many times does the star fit exactly on itself before returning to its original position?

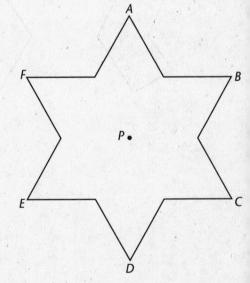

MODULE 4 | **LABSHEET** **4B**

Congruent Butterflies (Use with Question 21 on page 272.)

Directions

a. Predict where you think the line of reflection might be located for a reflection that makes the top butterfly fit exactly on the bottom butterfly. Lightly sketch this line.

b. Choose a point *A* on the top butterfly and find its image *A′* on the bottom butterfly. Label the points.

c. Construct the perpendicular bisector of $\overline{AA'}$ to find the line of reflection.

d. Use paper folding or a MIRA® to check your line of reflection.

e. How close is the line of reflection to your first prediction?

Fox Belt Design (Use with Question 24 on page 272.)

Directions Draw all the lines of symmetry on each part of the belt design shown below.

a.

b.

c.

MODULE 4   **LABSHEET** 4C

Rotated Stick Figure (Use with Exercises 46 and 47 on page 278.)

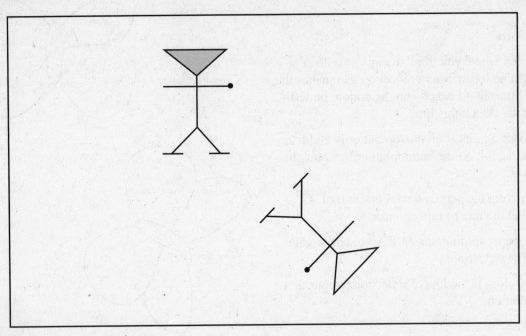

Directions

a. Trace the shaded Stick Figure. Experiment with rotating the shaded figure using different centers of rotation. Then estimate the location of the center and the amount of rotation that will describe the movement of the shaded figure to its image.

b. Draw a segment connecting any point on the shaded figure with its image.

c. Construct the perpendicular bisector of the segment drawn in part (b).

d. Repeat parts (b) and (c) for a new set of points on the figure and image.

e. The two perpendicular bisectors intersect at the center of rotation. Label it *C*. Use your tracing to test that *C* is the center of rotation.

f. How does the location of the center of rotation compare with your estimate in part (a)?

g. Use a protractor to measure the amount of rotation. How does it compare with your estimate in part (a)?

Name _____ Date _____

MODULE 4

Practice and Applications

For use with Section 4

For use with Exploration 1

1. Determine whether each shape has rotational symmetry. For each shape that has rotational symmetry, find all its rotational symmetries.

a.

b.

c.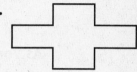

d.

e.

f.

For use with Exploration 2

2. Tell whether each diagram shows a reflection of the original figure across the line.

a.

b.

c.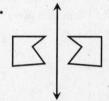

3. Tell whether the figures in each pair are congruent.

a.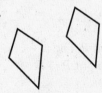

b.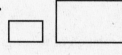

c.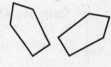

4. For each figure, tell whether the line shown is a line of symmetry. If it is not, explain why not.

a.

b.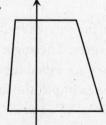

c.

Name _____   Date _____

The Math of Motion   Rotations and Reflections

GOAL   **LEARN HOW TO:** • rotate a figure
• describe a rotation
• identify rotational symmetries
• identify a reflection
• identify lines of symmetry

AS YOU: • study designs used in artwork
• explore mirror images in art

Exploration 1: Rotations and Symmetry

Rotations

A **rotation** turns a figure about a fixed point, called the **center of rotation**,
a certain number of degrees either clockwise or counterclockwise. The
new figure is the **image** of the original figure.

Example

Use a protractor to measure the angle of rotation.
Then describe the rotation of the original figure
in two ways.

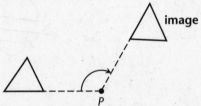

■ Sample Response ■

The image is a 120° clockwise rotation of the original figure about point *P*. The
image is a 240° counterclockwise rotation of the original figure about point *P*.

Rotational Symmetry

A figure that fits exactly on itself after being rotated less than
360° about a point has **rotational symmetry**. The angle measures
at which a figure has rotational symmetry are called the
rotational symmetries of the figure. For example, the figure at
the right has rotational symmetries of 90°, 180°, and 270°.

Name _____   Date _____

Exploration 2: Reflections and Symmetry

Reflections

A **reflection** flips a figure across a line. The line is the **line of reflection**. Each point on the original figure and its image are the same distance from the line of reflection. If you draw a line segment from a point on the original figure to its image, the perpendicular bisector of that segment is the line of reflection. The original figure and its image (after a reflection *or* a rotation) are **congruent**, since they are the same size and shape.

Each point where two sides of a triangle meet is called a **vertex of the triangle**. The plural of vertex is *vertices*.

Example

Tell whether each diagram shows a reflection of the original figure across the line.

a.
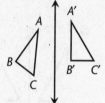

b.
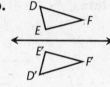

Sample Response

a. No, the figure is not a reflection across the line. If $\overline{AA'}$ is drawn, it does not form a right angle with the given line.

b. Yes, the figure is a reflection across the line. If segments are drawn between the corresponding vertices of the two triangles, each of these segments would form a right angle with the given line.

Line Symmetry

A figure has **line symmetry** if one half of the figure is the reflection of the other half across a line. The line of reflection is a **line of symmetry** for the figure. For example, the figure at the right has two lines of symmetry, as shown.

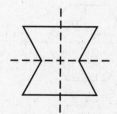

Name _____   Date _____

MODULE 4 Study Guide: Practice & Application Exercises

For use with Section 4

Exploration 1

1. Draw a triangle. Mark and label a point below the triangle to use as the center of rotation. Then draw the image of the triangle after a 160° clockwise rotation.

Determine whether each shape has rotational symmetry. For each shape that has rotational symmetry, find all its rotational symmetries.

2.

3.

4.

5.

Exploration 2

Tell whether each diagram shows a reflection of the original figure across the given line.

6.

7.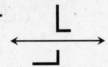

8.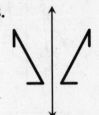

Tell whether the figures in each pair are congruent.

9.

10.

11.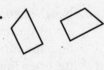

For each figure, tell whether the line shown is a line of symmetry. If it is not, explain why not.

12.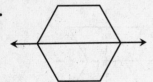

13.

14.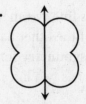

Name _____ Date _____

1. Find all the rotational symmetries of the figure.

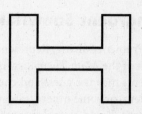

2. Does the figure in Question 1 have line symmetry? If so, draw the lines of symmetry. If not, explain why not.

3. Is the given line a line of symmetry? Explain.

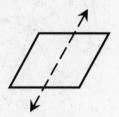

4. Tell whether the diagram shows a reflection.

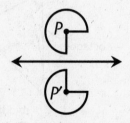

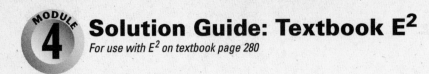

Solution Guide: Textbook E²

4 *For use with E² on textbook page 280*

Congruent Snowflakes

The Problem Solving, Representations, Mathematical Language, and Presentation
Scales of the *Math Thematics Assessment Scales* should be used to assess student work.
Students may use guess and check, work backward, use a picture, solve a simpler
problem, or some other strategy or combination of strategies to solve this problem.
Students should clearly show the steps to create a congruent snowflake design. The
extent of the mathematical language they use will depend on the strategy they employ.
More consideration should be given to the mathematical language scale for students
who analyze the snowflake design in terms of symmetry and angle measure. The sample
response below shows part of a student's solution.

Partial Solution

Since the snowflake design is an octagon with 4 lines of symmetry, I
decided to make a copy of the snowflake and draw the lines of symmetry
on it to identify what design repeats in the snowflake. I could see that the
basic design was a scalene triangle with cut-out pieces. The triangle is
scalene because the octagon is not regular. I sketched the design on the right.

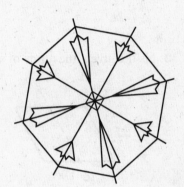

I decided to get the basic octagon shape first. I would need to fold the
paper 3 times to get the 8 sections, since each additional fold would
result in 2^n sections (n = the number of folds). $2^n = 8$ gives a value of 3
for n. I used a square sheet of paper and folded it in half, in half again,
and in half once more.

Then I measured the two long sides of the triangle on the copy. The lengths were
3.5 cm and 3.7 cm. So I measured the same distances from the center of my section (the
point) along the outside edges, drew a segment connecting the points, and cut along the
segment. My unfolded design was the same shape and size as the snowflake in the book.

Next I re-folded my design, and tried to figure out how to make the cuts for the
hexagons, middle square, and octagons on the snowflake. I could see that the
cut for the middle square had to be perpendicular to the 3.5 cm edge and start
about 4 mm from the point. I made the cut and checked to see if the square
was right. It was! To get the hexagon and octagon, I measured the location of
the vertices on the copy and used the measurements to sketch the figures on
my sector. When I made my cuts, the unfolded design was pretty close to the
snowflake in the book. I probably could have done better if I had measured
some of the angles too, and not just lengths.

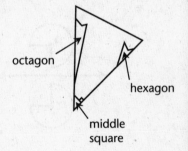

octagon

hexagon

middle
square

Name _____   Date _____

The Chinese Checkerboard

The Situation

Chinese checkers is a modern version of a 19th century English game called *Halma*. (Halma is a Greek word meaning "leap.") The new game became popular in the United States in the 1930s and is still played today.

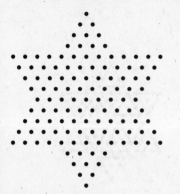

In the game, colored marbles are moved on a game board made up of holes or depressions arranged in the design shown at the left.

The Problem

How many holes are there on a Chinese checkerboard?

Something to Think About

- Are the holes in the checkerboard arranged in any particular patterns?
- Suppose each point of the star contained 15 holes instead of ten. How would you find the number of holes in this case?

Present Your Results

Describe at least three patterns that could be used to find the number of holes. Explain how to use the patterns to find the number of holes. Show any drawings or tables that you used to solve the problem.

Solution Guide: Alternate E²

For use with Module 4

The Chinese Checkerboard

Solutions to this problem will vary. All of the *Math Thematics Assessment Scales* can be used to assess students' solutions.

The sample response below shows part of a student's solution. Note that a student only needs to find three ways to count the holes.

Partial Solution

I found a lot of different ways to count the holes. Some of them are shown below. I tried to find a pattern in the expressions by writing them another way.

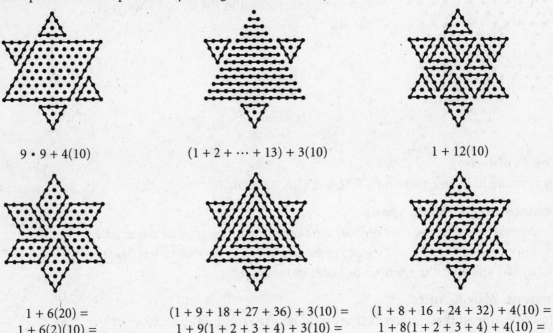

$9 \cdot 9 + 4(10)$

$(1 + 2 + \cdots + 13) + 3(10)$

$1 + 12(10)$

$$1 + 6(20) =$$
$$1 + 6(2)(10) =$$
$$1 + 12(10)$$

$$(1 + 9 + 18 + 27 + 36) + 3(10) =$$
$$1 + 9(1 + 2 + 3 + 4) + 3(10) =$$
$$1 + 9(10) + 3(10) =$$
$$1 + 12(10)$$

$$(1 + 8 + 16 + 24 + 32) + 4(10) =$$
$$1 + 8(1 + 2 + 3 + 4) + 4(10) =$$
$$1 + 8(10) + 4(10) =$$
$$1 + 12(10)$$

I found a rule for finding the number of holes in a Chinese checkerboard by trying a simpler problem and looking for a pattern.

Number of holes in a point of the star	1	3	6	10	...	n
Pattern for counting holes				See third method above		
Total number of holes	$1 + 12(1) = 13$	$1 + 12(3) = 37$	$1 + 12(6) = 73$	$1 + 12(10) = 121$	...	$1 + 12(n)$

A Chinese checkerboard with 15 holes in each point of the star would have $1 + 12(15) = 181$ holes.

Other Considerations

• You may want to photocopy a page with six Chinese checkerboard dot arrangements.

Name _____   Date _____

Warm-Up Exercises

For use with Section 5

Multiply.

1. $56 \cdot 23$

2. $4\frac{2}{3} \cdot \frac{5}{8}$

3. $4.52 \cdot 3.4$

Divide.

4. $625 \div 25$

5. $\frac{72}{12}$

6. $6.496 \div 3.2$

ANSWERS

1. 1288   2. $2\frac{11}{12}$ 3. 15.368   4. 25   5. 6   6. 2.03

MODULE 4   **LABSHEET** (**5A**)

Football Field (Use with Questions 1 and 2 on pages 281–282.)

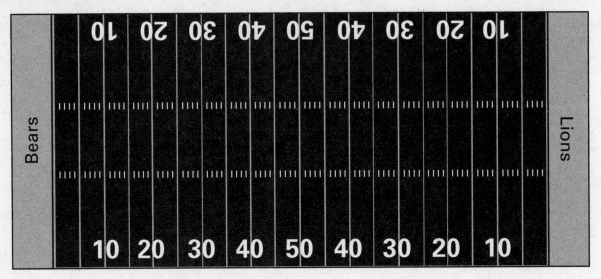

Multiplication Table (Use with Questions 5 and 6 on page 283.)

Directions

• Fill in the products you know.

• Look for patterns to fill in the remaining products.

×	3	2	1	0	–1	–2	–3
3							
2							
1							
0							
–1							
–2							
–3							

Math Thematics, Book 2
Teacher's Resource Book, Modules 3 and 4

Name _____   Date _____

 Practice and Applications
For use with Section 5

For use with Exploration 1

1. Find each product.

   a. $(-3)(7)$ **b.** $12(-5)$ **c.** $6(-9)$

   d. $(-5)(-4)$ **e.** $(14)(-9)$ **f.** $(-2)(53)$

   g. $40(-6)$ **h.** $(-12)(12)$ **i.** $(-25)(-5)$

   j. $(-15)(7)$ **k.** $(-16)(-8)$ **l.** $(-18)(20)$

2. Write and solve the related multiplication equation to find each quotient.

   a. $45 \div (-9) = x$ **b.** $-18 \div 3 = x$ **c.** $-8 \div (-2) = x$

   d. $-25 \div 25 = x$ **e.** $48 \div (-12) = x$ **f.** $-42 \div 7 = x$

3. Find each quotient.

   a. $36 \div (-6)$ **b.** $\dfrac{54}{-9}$ **c.** $-63 \div (-9)$

   d. $\dfrac{-42}{6}$ **e.** $\dfrac{-96}{-4}$ **f.** $\dfrac{120}{-5}$

   g. $45 \div (-3)$ **h.** $\dfrac{99}{-9}$ **i.** $-168 \div (-6)$

   j. $-160 \div 4$ **k.** $\dfrac{-300}{6}$ **l.** $-75 \div 3$

4. Find each product.

   a. $(-4)(-3)(-5)$ **b.** $(2)(-26)(-1)$ **c.** $4(5)(-3)(6)$

   d. $(-3)(-5)(-7)(-2)$ **e.** $(-8)(-5)(9)$ **f.** $2(-25)(-8)(-5)(-4)$

5. Find each product or quotient.

   a. $56 \div (-8)$ **b.** $(-15)(6)$ **c.** $\dfrac{270}{-9}$

   d. $(41)(-18)$ **e.** $\dfrac{-64}{-4}$ **f.** $(-5)(-9)(-2)$

6. On January 1, the temperature reading was $-5°C$. One month later on
   February 1, the temperature reading was 3 times that of January 1.
   What was the temperature reading on February 1?

(continued)

Name _____ Date _____

MODULE 4

For use with Exploration 2

7. Evaluate each expression.

  a. $-12 + 4^2(-8)$

  b. $\left(\frac{1}{4} + \frac{3}{8}\right) \div \frac{1}{2}$

  c. $(2.6)(4) - 5.6$

  d. $2\frac{2}{3} \cdot \frac{5}{6} + 15$

  e. $-118 \div (-8 + 4)$

  f. $6^2 \cdot (28.6 - 5.28)$

  g. $4.9 \cdot 6 - 26$

  h. $-98 \div (-8 - 6)$

  i. $-16 + 5^2(-2)$

8. Evaluate each expression when $a = \frac{2}{3}$, $b = 8$, and $c = 1\frac{1}{4}$.

  a. $6 \div c$

  b. ab

  c. $3a + c$

  d. $6 - ac$

  e. $12 \div a$

  f. $bc - a$

  g. $8 \div c$

  h. $4c - b$

  i. $3b + 2a$

9. Evaluate each expression when $q = 3.2$, $r = 0.4$, and $s = 6$.

  a. $4q$

  b. $q \div r$

  c. $(q - r) \cdot s$

  d. $s \div r$

  e. $5r + q$

  f. $(q + r) \div s$

  g. $4q \div r$

  h. $(s + r) \div q$

  i. $(s - q) \cdot r$

10. Evaluate each expression when $x = -4$, $y = 7$, and $z = -6$.

  a. $32 - z$

  b. $15x \div z$

  c. $y + z \cdot x$

  d. $(45 - y) \div x$

  e. $x \cdot z - 10$

  f. $z - 3y$

  g. $y \cdot x + 8$

  h. $y \cdot z \div x$

  i. $z - x \cdot y$

  j. $\frac{66}{z}$

  k. $\frac{x}{-2}$

  l. $5z + 5$

11. A phone company charges $0.50 for the first minute of a long distance telephone call and $0.15 for each additional minute. Each call is rounded up to the nearest minute.

  a. Let $x =$ the number of additional minutes after the first minute. Write an expression that represents the total cost of the call for any number of minutes.

  b. How much will a 16-minute call cost?

Name _____ Date _____

Study Guide
For use with Section 5

Special Effects   Multiplication and Division of Integers

GOAL **LEARN HOW TO:** • multiply and divide integers
    • evaluate expressions containing decimals, fractions, or integers
  As you: • move along a number line
    • explore how larger-than-life video clips are created

Exploration 1: Multiplying and Dividing Integers

Properties of Multiplication

The **commutative property of multiplication** says you can *change the order* of numbers in a multiplication problem and still get the same product.

The **associative property of multiplication** says that you can *change the grouping* when you multiply numbers and still get the same product.

The product or quotient of two integers is:

- *positive* when both integers are positive or when both integers are negative.

$-5 \cdot (-3) = 15$ $-12 \div (-6) = 2$
$6 \cdot 4 = 24$ $32 \div 8 = 4$

- *negative* when one of the integers is positive and the other integer is negative.

$4 \cdot (-2) = -8$ $-18 \div 9 = -2$

Exploration 2: Evaluating Expressions

You evaluate expressions containing fractions, decimals, or integers the same way you evaluate whole number expressions. Follow the order of operations and evaluate expressions inside grouping symbols first. Remember that a fraction bar is a grouping symbol.

> **Example**
>
> Evaluate the expression $\dfrac{(-3) \cdot 4^2 - 5}{-7 + (-2)}$.
>
> **■ Sample Response ■**
>
> $$\frac{(-3) \cdot 4^2 - 5}{-7 + (-2)} = \frac{(-3) \cdot 16 - 5}{-9}$$
>
> $$= \frac{-48 - 5}{-9} = \frac{-53}{-9} = \frac{53}{9}, \text{ or } 5\frac{8}{9}$$

Name _____   Date _____

Study Guide: Practice & Application Exercises
For use with Section 5

Exploration 1

For Exercises 1–15, find each product or quotient.

1. $(-6)(5)$ **2.** $24(-2)$ **3.** $-18 \div (-2)$

4. $550 \div (-5)$ **5.** $(-7)(-4)$ **6.** $-114 \div 3$

7. $45 \div (-9)$ **8.** $(-2)(-2)(-5)$ **9.** $-63 \div (-7)$

10. $(-8)(7)$ **11.** $-42 \div (-6)$ **12.** $(-13)(-5)$

13. $(-102) \div 2$ **14.** $-81 \div 9$ **15.** $(-7)(-1)(-5)$

16. The temperature dropped 3°C each day last week. How many degrees must be *added* to the temperature at the beginning of the week to find the temperature at the end of the seven days?

17. James withdrew $15 from his bank account 4 different times this month. What amount must he *add* to his original balance to find his new monthly balance?

Exploration 2

Evaluate each expression.

18. $-3 + (-2)(-1)$ **19.** $\left(\dfrac{5}{8} + \dfrac{5}{12}\right) \div \dfrac{5}{6}$ **20.** $-3 - (-15) \div (-5)$

21. $14.02 - 0.27(-8)$ **22.** $-6(41 - (-3))$ **23.** $(-2.3)(-5.1) + 1$

24. $\left(\dfrac{1}{10} + \dfrac{3}{5}\right)(-2)$ **25.** $0.12 \div 0.4 + 5$ **26.** $-39 \div (-5 - 2)$

For Exercises 27–32, evaluate each expression when $x = -2$, $y = 0.5$, and $z = 4$.

27. $\dfrac{z}{x}$ **28.** $2y + (-5)x \cdot z$ **29.** $23 - x$

30. $(x + z) \cdot y$ **31.** $z - y + x$ **32.** $15x$

33. Write a word problem that can be solved by evaluating $2x - 3$ for $x = 5$. Then solve the problem.

Math Thematics, Book 2
Teacher's Resource Book, Modules 3 and 4

Name _____ Date _____

Quick Quiz
For use after Section 5

1. Find the product $(-2)(-4)(5)$.

2. Find the quotient $140 \div (-7)$.

3. Evaluate $4\frac{3}{4} - 2\frac{1}{3} \cdot \frac{3}{14}$.

4. Copy and add grouping symbols to make the statement true.

$-2 \cdot 3 + (-1) \div 6 - 8 = 2$

5. Evaluate when $a = \frac{2}{5}$ and $b = 0.64$.

$4 \cdot a - b + a \cdot b$

Name _____ Date _____

MODULE 4 Warm-Up Exercises
For use with Section 6

Decide whether each pair of figures is congruent. Explain your reasoning.

1.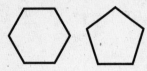

2.

3.

Use mental math to solve.

4. $-7 + x = 4$

5. $p + 13 = 42$

6. $12 + m = 8$

ANSWERS

1. No; not the same shape   2. Yes; same exact size and shape, one is turned differently   3. No; same shape, but not the same size   4. 11   5. 29   6. –4

Name _____   Date _____

Translating a Figure (Use with Question 9 on page 297.)

Directions

a. Suppose quadrilateral *WXYZ* shown below is translated using the
    transformation $(x + 1, y - 2)$. Use the directions *left* or *right* and *up* or *down*
    to describe the location of the image.

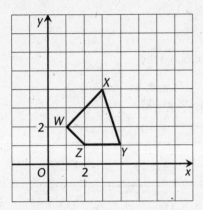

b. Complete the table. Identify the coordinates of the vertices of quadrilateral
    WXYZ. Then find the coordinates of the vertices of the image of quadrilateral
    WXYZ after the translation $(x + 1, y - 2)$.

	Coordinates of Vertices			
Original (figure *WXYZ*)	W(___, ___)	X(___, ___)	Y(___, ___)	Z(___, ___)
Image (figure *W'X'Y'Z'*)	W'(___, ___)	X'(___, ___)	Y'(___, ___)	Z'(___, ___)

c. Use your results from part (b) to draw the image of quadrilateral *WXYZ* on the
    coordinate plane.

d. How does the actual location of the image compare with your prediction in
    part (a)?

Name _____   Date _____

Stretching and Squashing a Figure (Use with Questions 14–16 on pages 298–299.)

Directions

a. Each member of your group should choose a different transformation from the list below.

  Transformation 1: $(3x, y)$ (Multiply the x-coordinate by 3.)

  Transformation 2: $(x, 3y)$ (Multiply the y-coordinate by 3.)

  Transformation 3: $(3x, 3y)$ (Multiply both the x-coordinate and the
                                                    y-coordinate by 3.)

b. Find the coordinates of the vertices of the image of figure $ABCDE$ for your transformation. Record the coordinates in the table.

Original (x, y)	$A(-2, 0)$	$B(-2, 1)$	$C(0, 2)$	$D(2, 1)$	$E(2, 0)$
Transformation (___ , ___)	$A'(\_\_, \_\_)$	$B'(\_\_, \_\_)$	$C'(\_\_, \_\_)$	$D'(\_\_, \_\_)$	$E'(\_\_, \_\_)$

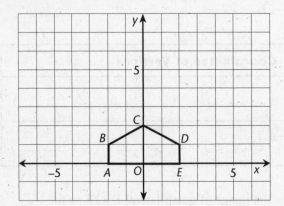

c. Use your results from part (b) to draw the image of figure $ABCDE$ on the coordinate plane.

d. Use your group's results from part (c). For each transformation, explain how the image of figure $ABCDE$ is different from the original figure. How are the image and the original figure alike?

Name _____   Date _____

Flag (Use with Question 21 on page 300 and Question 23 on page 301.)

Directions

a. Find the coordinates of the vertices of the image of the flag after the
    transformation $(2x + 3, 3y - 4)$. Record the coordinates in the table below.

	Image Points		
	x-coordinate **(2x + 3)**	**y-coordinate** **(3y – 4)**	**(x, y)**
$A(-1, 0)$	2(–1) + 3 = ____	3(0) – 4 = ____	A′(____ , ____)
$B(1, 2)$			B′(____ , ____)
$C(2, 3)$			C′(____ , ____)
$D(3, 1)$			D′(____ , ____)

b. Use the coordinates you found to draw the image of the flag on the
    coordinate plane.

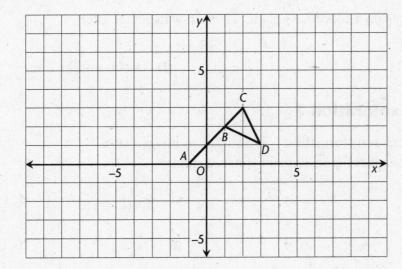

Name _____ Date _____

For use with Exploration 1

1. Tell whether each diagram shows a translation of the original figure. If not, explain why not.

a.  **b.** 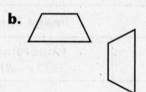 **c.**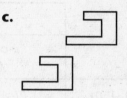

2. Write each translation using coordinates.

a. 5 units to the left

b. 8 units down

c. 6 units up

d. 4 units to the right

e. 2 units to the right and 6 units up

f. 3 units to the left and 5 units down

g. 5 units to the left and 1 unit up

h. 7 units to the right and 4 units down

3. Draw a rectangle on a coordinate plane. Then draw its image after each translation.

a. $(x + 2, y - 1)$

b. $(x - 3, y - 2)$

For use with Exploration 2

4. Tell whether each transformation will result in an image that is similar to the original figure. Explain your reasoning.

a. $\left(\frac{1}{3}x, 3y\right)$

b. $(6x, y)$

c. $\left(\frac{1}{4}x, \frac{1}{4}y\right)$

d. $\left(\frac{1}{3}x, \frac{1}{6}y\right)$

e. $(5x, 5y)$

f. $(x, 4y)$

g. $\left(2x, \frac{1}{2}y\right)$

h. $(4x, 2y)$

5. Suppose a computer animator wants to use the transformation $(x, 2y)$ to stretch the figure shown. Make a sketch of how the figure will look after the transformation.

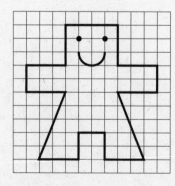

(continued)

Name _____ Date _____

Practice and Applications
For use with Section 6

For use with Exploration 3

6. Solve each equation. Check each solution.

   a. $3t + 8 = 23$ **b.** $\frac{n}{4} - 5 = 3$ **c.** $14 + 6y = -22$

   d. $4m - 6.2 = 1$ **e.** $8 + \frac{x}{9} = 8$ **f.** $-6b + 5 = 12$

   g. $\frac{p}{7} - 15 = 13$ **h.** $15h + 29 = 68$ **i.** $\frac{k}{8} + 0.7 = 6.8$

   j. $6x + 9 = 51$ **k.** $2y + 18 = -54$ **l.** $\frac{m}{9} - 0.2 = 0.5$

   m. $16t - 11 = 17$ **n.** $9 + \frac{k}{8} = 54$ **o.** $86 + 5r = 46$

7. Write an equation to represent each statement. Then solve the equation and check your solution.

   a. Five more than three times a number is thirty-two.

   b. A number divided by four and then decreased by six is six.

   c. Eight increased by the product of a number and seven is forty-three.

   d. Nine more than six times a number is eighty-one.

   e. A number divided by five and then decreased by four is three.

   f. Twelve increased by twice a number is twenty-eight.

8. A sports store charges a flat fee of $35 plus $8 per day to rent a canoe.

   a. Let x = the number of days a canoe is rented. Write an equation to show the cost c of renting a canoe.

   b. Suppose a person was charged $67 for renting a canoe. For how many days did the person rent the canoe?

9. Kent has a coupon for $5 off any shirt purchase from a department store. He buys three shirts and spends a total of $43 after using the coupon. Each shirt cost the same amount of money.

   a. Let x = the cost of one shirt. Write an equation to model the situation.

   b. What is the cost of one shirt?

Name _____ Date _____

4 **Study Guide**
For use with Section 6

Animation   Translations, Similarity, and Two-Step Equations

GOAL   **LEARN HOW TO:** • use coordinates to describe translations
• locate the image from a translation on a coordinate plane
• stretch or squash a figure in a coordinate plane
• identify similar figures
• solve two-step equations

AS YOU: • explore ways to create animations
• explore ways to make animation more realistic
• explore how to change both the shape and the location of an animated figure

Exploration 1: Translations

Transformations and Translations

A **transformation** is a change in a figure's shape, size, or location. Three types of transformations are reflections, rotations, and translations. Transformations can be described using coordinates. *Left* or *right* are directions used to describe the movement of figures on the horizontal axis, usually called the **x-axis**. *Up* or *down* describes movement on the vertical axis, usually called the **y-axis**.

A **translation** is a transformation that slides a figure to a new location. The image is congruent to the original figure.

Example

The coordinates of the vertices of $\triangle ABC$ are $A(4, 2)$, $B(7, 2)$, and $C(7, 3)$. Draw $\triangle ABC$ on a coordinate plane and translate it 1 unit to the left and 2 units down. Then use coordinates to describe the translation.

Sample Response

The coordinates of the vertices of the image triangle, $\triangle A'B'C'$, are $A'(3, 0)$, $B'(6, 0)$, and $C'(6, 1)$.

Using coordinates, if the original point is (x, y), then its image is $(x - 1, y - 2)$.

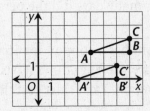

Name _____   Date _____

Exploration 2: Changing Size and Shape

Transformations that Stretch or Squash

You can stretch or squash a figure horizontally by multiplying the *x*-coordinates of all its points by the same factor, or vertically by multiplying the *y*-coordinates of all its points by the same factor. A factor greater than 1 stretches. A factor between 0 and 1 squashes. When you stretch or squash a figure horizontally and vertically by the same factor, the image is similar to the original figure. Figures are **similar** if they are the same shape, but not necessarily the same size.

The figure on the left below shows $\triangle ABC$ with vertices $A(-3, 0)$, $B(-3, 2)$, and $C(2, 0)$. The middle figure shows two transformations of $\triangle ABC$, a horizontal stretch where the *x*-coordinate of every point has been multiplied by 2 and a vertical squash where the *y*-coordinate of every point has been multiplied by $\frac{1}{2}$. The figure on the right shows a third transformation, one in which both coordinates of every point have been multiplied by 2. This image triangle is similar to the original triangle.

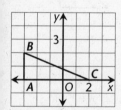 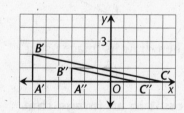 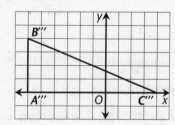

Exploration 3: Solving Two-Step Equations

You solve two-step equations by working backward through the order of operations using inverse operations.

Example
Solve the equation $5x + 3 = 13$.

Sample Response

Step 1 Subtract 3 from both sides. $5x + 3 - 3 = 13 - 3$
Step 2 Simplify both sides. $5x = 10$

Step 3 Divide both sides by 5. $\frac{5x}{5} = \frac{10}{5}$

Step 4 Simplify. $x = 2$

Name _____ Date _____

Study Guide: Practice & Application Exercises
For use with Section 6

Exploration 1

Tell whether each diagram shows a translation of the original figure. If not, explain why not.

1.    2. 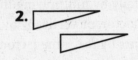   3.

For Exercises 4 and 5, write each translation using coordinates.

4. 8 units to the left and 1 unit down

5. 5 units to the right and 3 units up

6. Draw a rectangle on a coordinate plane. Then draw its image after the translation $(x + 4, y - 3)$.

Exploration 2

7. Tell which figures are similar.

A.   B.   C.   D.

8. Draw a rectangle on a coordinate plane. Then draw its image using the transformation $\left(2x, \dfrac{y}{2}\right)$.

Tell whether each transformation will result in an image that is similar to the original figure.

9. $(x, 3y)$ 10. $(2x, 2y)$ 11. $\left(\dfrac{1}{3}x, \dfrac{1}{9}y\right)$

Exploration 3

Solve each equation. Check each solution.

12. $3t + 8 = 32$ 13. $\dfrac{m}{5} - 2 = -12$ 14. $30 - 7x = 9$

15. $2x - 5 = 39$ 16. $\dfrac{y}{5} + 7 = 12$ 17. $4m + 16 = 28$

18. $14 + 3t = -16$ 19. $-27 + 5x = 8$ 20. $-7y - 25 = 17$

Name _____   Date _____

Quick Quiz

For use after Section 6

1. Describe a translation 2 units to the right and 5 units down using coordinates.

2. Which of the following will result in an image that is similar to the original figure?

   A. $\left(8x, \dfrac{1}{8}y\right)$ **B.** $\left(\dfrac{1}{5}x, \dfrac{1}{5}y\right)$ **C.** $(2x, y+2)$

3. Give an example of a transformation that will squash the figure vertically and stretch it horizontally. Draw its image and label the coordinates of the vertices.

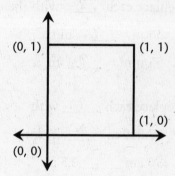

4. Solve $4t - 14 = 30$.

5. **a.** Write an equation to represent the following statement.

   Six added to a number divided by 4 is 36.

   b. Solve the equation you wrote in part (a).

Name _____   Date _____

Practice and Applications
For use after Sections 1–6

For use with Section 1

1. Find each product. Write each answer in lowest terms.

　a. $4 \cdot 2\frac{1}{6}$ 　　　　　**b.** $\frac{5}{8} \cdot \frac{2}{5}$ 　　　　　**c.** $2\frac{3}{5} \cdot 1\frac{3}{8}$

2. Find each quotient. Write each answer in lowest terms.

　a. $6 \div \frac{5}{6}$ 　　　　　**b.** $3\frac{1}{4} \div 1\frac{3}{4}$ 　　　　　**c.** $2\frac{4}{9} \div \frac{2}{3}$

For use with Section 2

3. Replace each ___?___ with the correct measure.

　a. 3 km = ___?___ mm 　　　　　　**b.** 850 m = ___?___ km

　c. 55 mm = ___?___ m 　　　　　　**d.** 6.3 cm = ___?___ m

4. Replace each ___?___ with >, <, or =.

　a. 27,000 m ___?___ 27 km 　　　　　**b.** 12 cm ___?___ 6 km

　c. 90 cm ___?___ 0.5 m 　　　　　　**d.** 48 mm ___?___ 4800 m

For use with Section 3

5. Find each product. Show your work.

　a. $0.4 \cdot 0.17$ 　　　　　**b.** $412 \cdot 1.18$ 　　　　　**c.** $1.8 \cdot 3.02$

6. Predict whether each product will be *greater than*, *less than*, or *equal to* the boldface number. Explain how you know.

　a. $3.7 \cdot 1.2$ 　　　　　**b.** $0.26 \cdot 0.95$ 　　　　　**c.** $0.048 \cdot 1$

7. Write each fraction as a decimal rounded to the nearest hundredth.

　a. $\frac{3}{14}$ 　　　　　**b.** $\frac{5}{9}$ 　　　　　**c.** $\frac{7}{12}$

8. Predict whether each quotient will be *greater than*, *less than*, or *equal to* the boldface number. Explain how you know.

　a. $41.85 \div 0.32$ 　　　　　**b.** $118\overline{)71.04}$ 　　　　　**c.** $612.9 \div 1$

(continued)

Name _____   Date _____

MODULE 4
Practice and Applications
For use after Sections 1–6

For use with Section 4

9. Tell whether the figures in each pair are congruent.

a. 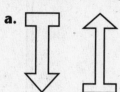   **b.** 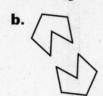   **c.**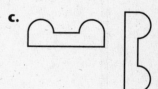

For use with Section 5

10. Find each product or quotient.

   a. $48 \div (-4)$ **b.** $(-14)(3)$ **c.** $\dfrac{350}{-5}$

   d. $(38)(-16)$ **e.** $\dfrac{-72}{-3}$ **f.** $(-6)(-4)(-3)$

11. A low temperature of –2°C occurred last week. This week the low temperature is 8 times that of last week. What is this week's low temperature?

12. Evaluate each expression when $x = -5$, $y = 3$, and $z = -4$.

   a. $32 - z$ **b.** $15x \div y$ **c.** $\dfrac{z}{-2}$

   d. $(48 - y) \div x$ **e.** $x \cdot z - 10$ **f.** $y \cdot z \div 6$

For use with Section 6

13. Write each translation using coordinates.

   a. 7 units to the right and 1 unit up   **b.** 2 units to the left and 8 units down

14. Tell whether each transformation will result in an image that is similar to the original figure. Explain your reasoning.

   a. $\left(\frac{1}{5}x, 5y\right)$ **b.** $(7x, y)$ **c.** $(6x, 6y)$

15. Solve each equation. Check each solution.

   a. $6t + 9 = 57$ **b.** $\dfrac{n}{5} - 8 = 3$ **c.** $19 + 4y = -13$

16. Eight more than six times a number is fifty. Write an equation to represent the statement. Then solve the equation.

MODULE 4   **PROJECT LABSHEET** **A**

Zoetrope Side Strips (Use with Project Question 3 on page 310.)

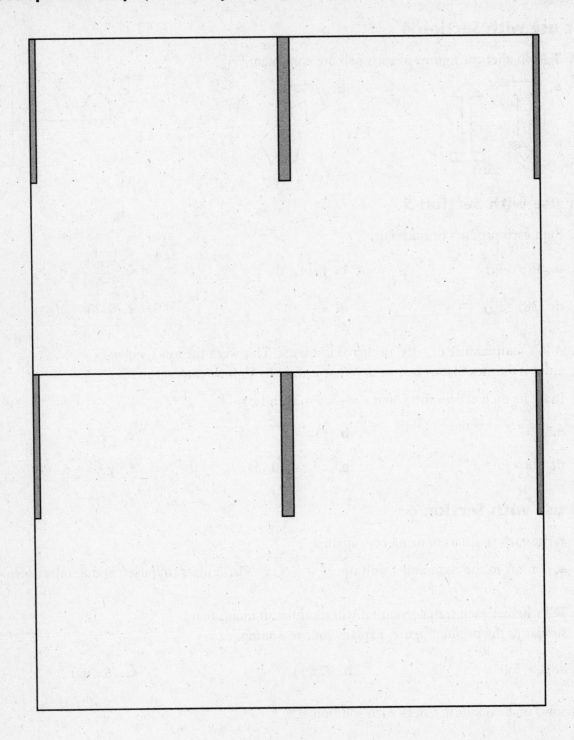

Name _____   Date _____

A Person Walking Forward (Use with Project Question 4 on page 311.)

MODULE 4   **PROJECT LABSHEET** C

A Person Walking Backward (Use with Project Question 5 on page 311.)

F1   F2

F3   F4

F5   F6

F7   F8

Name ______________________ Date ______________

MODULE 4

PROJECT LABSHEET D

Blank Zoetrope Strip D (Use with Project Questions 7 and 8 on page 312.)

F1 F2

F3 F4

F5 F6

F7 F8

MODULE 4   **PROJECT LABSHEET E**

Blank Zoetrope Strip E (Use with Project Question 11 on page 313.)

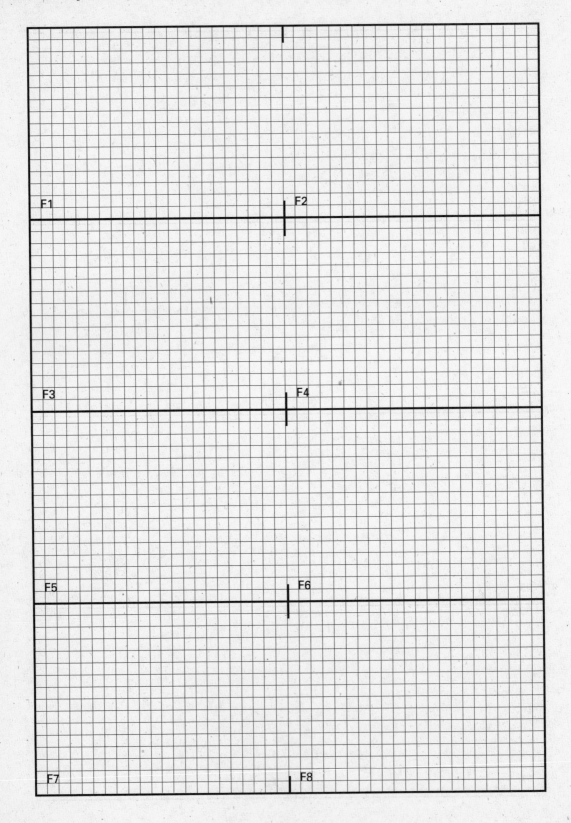

Name _____   Date _____

 **Test Form A**
For use after Module 4

Find the reciprocal of each number.

1. $\frac{2}{3}$

2. $2\frac{1}{4}$

Find each product or quotient. Write each answer in lowest terms.

3. $\frac{5}{8} \div \frac{3}{4}$

4. $\frac{3}{4} \cdot \frac{2}{9}$

5. $3\frac{1}{5} \cdot \frac{3}{4}$

6. $4\frac{2}{5} \div 2\frac{1}{5}$

Use benchmarks to decide if each measure is reasonable or unreasonable. If a measure is unreasonable, give a better estimate.

7. length of a calculator: 15 mm

8. length in a bathtub: 1.2 m

Write the correct measure in each blank.

9. 25 m = _____ cm

10. 3.1 km = _____ cm

11. 357 mm = _____ m

Find each product or quotient.

12. $14.8 \div 0.3$

13. $(70.3)(0.05)$

14. $6.43 \div 0.008$

Write each fraction as a decimal.

15. $\frac{13}{9}$

16. $\frac{3}{20}$

17. Explain the difference between a terminating and a repeating decimal.
   Give an example of each.

Test Form A
For use after Module 4

18. Tell whether the figure shown below has rotational symmetry. If so, find all its rotational symmetries.

19. Tell whether the diagram below shows a reflection of the shaded figure across the given line. If not, explain why not.

Find each product or quotient.

20. $14(-2)$

21. $-50 \div 5$

22. $(-2)(11)(-4)$

23. $-120 \div (-30)$

Evaluate each expression.

24. $14.7 \div 0.7 - 3.2 \cdot 5$

25. $\dfrac{6^2 - 4(-2)}{6 - 10}$

For Questions 26 and 27, use quadrilateral *ABCD* shown at the right.

26. a. Suppose you want to translate quadrilateral *ABCD* 2 units to the left and 4 units down. Describe the transformation using coordinates.

b. Draw the image of quadrilateral *ABCD* after the translation in part (a).

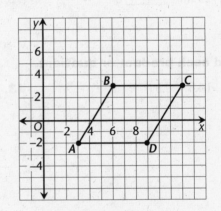

27. Use the transformation $\left(\dfrac{x}{3}, 2y\right)$ for parts (a) and (b).

a. Predict how the size, the shape, or the location of the image of quadrilateral *ABCD* will be different from that of the original figure.

b. Draw the image after the transformation.

c. Is the image similar to the original figure? Why or why not?

Solve each equation. Check each solution.

28. $8x - 3 = 117$

29. $\dfrac{y}{4} + 3 = 5$

Name _____   Date _____

Test Form B

For use after Module 4

Find the reciprocal of each number.

1. $\frac{5}{8}$

2. $3\frac{1}{7}$

Find each product or quotient. Write each answer in lowest terms.

3. $\frac{7}{8} \div \frac{11}{16}$

4. $\frac{2}{3} \cdot \frac{9}{16}$

5. $3\frac{1}{3} \cdot \frac{4}{5}$

6. $4\frac{7}{8} \div 1\frac{4}{9}$

Use benchmarks to decide if each measure is reasonable or unreasonable. If a measure is unreasonable, give a better estimate.

7. length of a couch: 2 m

8. length of an index finger: 2.8 cm

Write the correct measure in each blank.

9. 420 cm = _____ m

10. 38 mm = _____ cm

11. 7.2 km = _____ m

Find each product or quotient.

12. $16.7 \div 0.4$

13. $(61.9)(0.02)$

14. $14.21 \div 0.007$

Write each fraction as a decimal.

15. $\frac{5}{3}$

16. $\frac{11}{20}$

17. Explain the difference between a terminating and a repeating decimal. Give an example of each.

Test Form B
For use after Module 4

18. Tell whether the figure shown below has rotational symmetry. If so, find all its rotational symmetries.

19. Tell whether the diagram below shows a reflection of the shaded figure across the given line. If not, explain why not.

Find each product or quotient.

20. $20(-7)$

21. $-55 \div 11$

22. $(-3)(2)(-4)$

23. $-240 \div (-60)$

Evaluate each expression.

24. $(20.8 - 3.8 \cdot 4) \div 0.7$

25. $\dfrac{4^3 + (6^2)(-3)}{7 - (-4)}$

For Questions 26 and 27, use quadrilateral *ABCD* shown at the right.

26. a. Suppose you want to translate quadrilateral *ABCD* 3 units to the right and 5 units up. Describe the transformation using coordinates.

  b. Draw the image of quadrilateral *ABCD* after the translation in part (a).

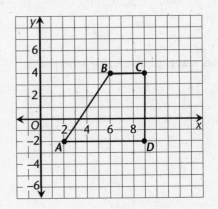

27. Use the transformation $\left(\dfrac{x}{2}, 3y\right)$ for parts (a) and (b).

  a. Predict how the size, the shape, or the location of the image of quadrilateral *ABCD* will be different from that of the original figure.

  b. Draw the image after the transformation.

  c. Is the image similar to the original figure? Why or why not?

Solve each equation. Check each solution.

28. $6x - 7 = 65$

29. $\dfrac{y}{5} + 11 = -5$

Name _____   Date _____

1. What are the rotational symmetries of this figure?

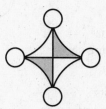

- **a.** 90°, 180°, 270°
- **b.** 180°
- **c.** 120°, 240°
- **d.** There are none.

2. Lori ran 400 m. How many millimeters did Lori run?
- **a.** 4,000
- **b.** 40,000
- **c.** 400,000
- **d.** 4,000,000

3. Find the product $\frac{5}{12} \cdot 3\frac{3}{7}$ and express the answer in lowest terms.
- **a.** $\frac{20}{21}$
- **b.** $1\frac{1}{3}$
- **c.** $1\frac{3}{7}$
- **d.** $1\frac{10}{19}$

4. Find the quotient $3\frac{3}{4} \div 2\frac{1}{2}$.
- **a.** $1\frac{1}{2}$
- **b.** $2\frac{5}{8}$
- **c.** $6\frac{1}{4}$
- **d.** $9\frac{3}{8}$

5. How much does 1.84 lb of steak cost if the price is $4.65/lb?
- **a.** $6.49
- **b.** $7.70
- **c.** $8.56
- **d.** $9.43

6. Write $\frac{7}{18}$ as a repeating decimal.
- **a.** $0.\overline{42}$
- **b.** $0.4\overline{2}$
- **c.** $0.3\overline{8}$
- **d.** $0.38\overline{}$

7. Which of the following statements is true?

p

- **a.** Line p is the only line of symmetry.
- **b.** The figure does not have rotational symmetry.
- **c.** The figure has two lines of symmetry, one vertical and one horizontal.
- **d.** The figure has rotational symmetry of 90° and 270°.

8. Which of the following transformations gives an image that is similar to the original figure?
- **a.** $(3x + 1, y + 1)$
- **b.** $(x + 2, 2y)$
- **c.** $(x, 3y)$
- **d.** $(4x, 4y)$

9. Which of these products and quotients represents the largest number?
- **a.** $\frac{-60}{5}$
- **b.** $(-2)(-1)(-5)$
- **c.** $(-3)(-4)$
- **d.** $(-1)(-2)(-2)(-2)$

10. Evaluate $\frac{4}{5} - \left(\frac{1}{4} \cdot \frac{2}{3} - \frac{3}{4} \div 3 \right)$.
- **a.** $\frac{27}{60}$
- **b.** $\frac{4}{5}$
- **c.** $\frac{53}{60}$
- **d.** $\frac{-1}{20}$

11. Use coordinates to describe a translation 5 units to the right and 4 units down.
- **a.** $(x - 4, y + 5)$
- **b.** $(x + 5, y - 4)$
- **c.** $(x + 5, y + 4)$
- **d.** $(x + 4, y - 5)$

12. Solve $7 - \frac{a}{2} = -3$.
- **a.** −5
- **b.** −2
- **c.** 20
- **d.** 5

Name _____ Date _____

Module Performance Assessment
For use after Module 4

An animator is experimenting with using different techniques
to change the size, shape, or position of the figure at the right, which
represents a head with a face:

Step 1: Trace the figure on a piece of paper. Does the figure show line
symmetry? If so, draw all its lines of symmetry. Does the figure show
rotational symmetry? If so, describe its rotational symmetries.

Step 2: The diameter of the figure shown above is 1.5 cm. Estimate its
circumference. Without using a calculator, find the actual circumference
and compare it with your estimate (use 3.14 for π).

Step 3: Suppose the animator wants to enlarge the figure until its diameter is
8 cm. What decimal enlargement is needed? Could the animator use
exactly this enlargement? Explain.

Step 4: Would dividing by a fraction less than 1 be a good way to
shrink the size of the figure? Explain.

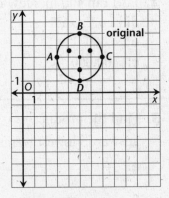

Step 5: The original figure is shown at the right on a coordinate
grid. Find its image points A', B', C', and D' after the
transformation $(x + 2, y - 8)$, and graph the results.
Is the image a translation of the original figure? Is it a
reflection of the original figure over the x-axis? Explain.

Step 6: Suppose the animator uses squash and stretch techniques
to change the shape and/or location of the circle that forms
the head of the original figure, as shown below.

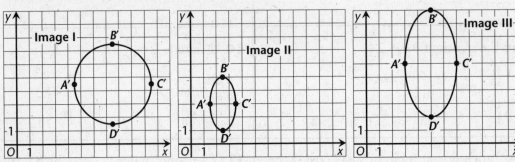

a. Explain which of the following transformations was used to create
each image:

   i. $\left(\dfrac{x}{2}, y\right)$ ii. $\left(\dfrac{3}{2}x, \dfrac{3}{2}y\right)$ iii. $(x, 2y)$

b. Are any of the images similar to the original figure? Explain.

Name _____   Date _____

Cumulative Test
For use after Modules 3 and 4

1. Tell whether the set of side lengths 12 in., 8 in., and 6 in. *can* or *cannot* form a triangle. If they can, tell whether the triangle is *isosceles*, *equilateral*, or *scalene*.

Find the circumference of a circle with each measure. Use 3.14 for π and round answers to the nearest tenth.

2. diameter = 18 in.

3. radius = 40 ft

4. **a.** Draw a line segment $1\frac{7}{8}$ in. long.

   b. Construct the perpendicular bisector of the segment.

5. Find the prime factorization of 210.

6. Find the greatest common factor (GCF) of 22, 44, 176.

7. Find the least common multiple (LCM) of 4, 5, 15.

Write the correct symbol, >, <, or = in each blank.

8. $\frac{11}{12}$ _____ $\frac{14}{15}$

9. $\frac{15}{24}$ _____ $\frac{35}{56}$

Find each sum or difference. Write answers in lowest terms.

10. $1\frac{1}{4} + 3\frac{5}{8}$

11. $3\frac{7}{9} - 1\frac{1}{6}$

Name _____   Date _____

Cumulative Test
For use after Modules 3 and 4

Find each product or quotient. Write each answer in lowest terms.

12. $4\frac{3}{8} \div 1\frac{1}{4}$ **13.** $\frac{7}{8} \div \frac{3}{4}$ **14.** $5\frac{1}{4} \cdot 1\frac{2}{7}$

15. Write $\frac{4}{11}$ as a decimal. Is the decimal *terminating* or *repeating*?

Write the correct measure in each blank.

16. 16 ft = _____ yd   **17.** $1\frac{1}{2}$ yd = _____ in.   **18.** 15 cm = _____ m

Find each product or quotient.

19. $103 \div 0.02$ **20.** $0.003 \cdot 1.3$ **21.** $150 \div (-10)$ **22.** $(-4)(-12)(2)$

23. Tell whether the figure at the right has line or rotational symmetry. If the figure has line symmetry, copy the figure and draw its lines of symmetry. If it has rotational symmetry, find all of its rotational symmetries.

Solve each equation. Check each solution.

24. $\frac{x}{8} = 112$ **25.** $5a - 3 = -23$

26. a. Refer to the figure at the right. Use coordinates to describe the transformation that will move the triangle 2 units to the left and 5 units up.

b. Draw the image after the translation in part (a).

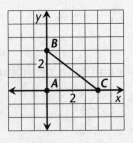

Mid-Year Test
For use after Modules 1–4

Find each sum or difference.

1. $(-4) + 9$

2. $8 + (-12)$

3. $7 - 13$

4. $(-3) - 7$

5. $2\frac{3}{4} + 4\frac{1}{8}$

6. $3\frac{2}{3} + 2\frac{1}{2}$

7. $4\frac{5}{8} - 1\frac{1}{4}$

8. $8\frac{1}{2} - 5\frac{3}{4}$

Find each product or quotient. Write each answer in lowest terms.

9. $\frac{3}{8} \cdot \frac{3}{5}$

10. $3\frac{4}{5} \cdot 2\frac{1}{2}$

11. $\frac{7}{8} \div \frac{3}{4}$

12. $7 \div 2\frac{1}{3}$

Find each product or quotient.

13. $(-7)5$

14. $(-12)(-4)$

15. $40 \div (-5)$

16. $-123 \div 3$

17. $12.36 \cdot 10^5$

18. $12.36 \cdot 0.001$

19. $12.36 \div 10,000$

20. $12.36 \div 0.01$

21. $(4.2)(0.06)$

22. $(15)(3.7)$

23. $143.7 \div 0.02$

24. $3.7 \div 0.9$

Evaluate each expression.

25. $\frac{4 + (2 \cdot 5)}{8 - 6}$

26. $4 + 5^2 - 3 \cdot 5$

27. $15 - (4 + 2) + 3 \cdot 4$

28. $|-9| + |-5|$

29. $|3 - 7|$

30. $-5 + 2 \cdot (-3 + 5)$

Replace each ___?___ with >, <, or =.

31. $\frac{24}{36}$ __?__ $\frac{6}{9}$

32. $\frac{7}{8}$ __?__ $\frac{11}{12}$

33. $\frac{19}{36}$ __?__ $\frac{12}{24}$

Solve. Check each answer.

34. $17 = 8 + y$

35. $15 + x = -7$

36. $15 = z - (-7)$

37. $128 = 8y$

38. $\frac{x}{6} = 42$

39. $4b + 5 = 37$

For Questions 40–43, evaluate each expression when $a = 7$, $b = -1$, $x = 4$, and $y = 2$.

40. $9x$

41. $y - a$

42. $a + b$

43. $4x + 2y$

For Questions 44–46, find the slope of a line with each rise and run.

44. rise 3
run 6

45. rise 8
run 2

46. rise 5
run 15

Mid-Year Test
For use after Modules 1–4

47. Find the number of degrees the minute hand of a clock rotates in 10 minutes.

48. Use the following sequence: 4, 8, 12, 16, …

    a. Make a table for the sequence.

    b. Draw a graph for the sequence, using the coordinate grid at the right.

    c. Write an equation for the sequence.

    d. Predict the 100th term.

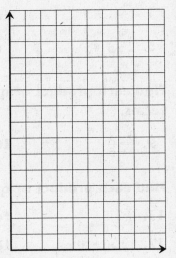

For Questions 49–51, refer to the spinners below. Suppose an experiment consists of spinning each of the two spinners. The resulting numbers are then added.

Spinner A   Spinner B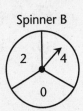

	Spinner B		
Spinner A	**0**	**2**	**4**
1	?	?	?
3	?	?	?
5	?	?	?

49. Complete the table above to show the sums (outcomes) that can occur.

50. Find the theoretical probability of each outcome.

51. If you spin the spinners 90 times, how many times would you expect to get a sum of either 3 or 9?

52. List the following integers in order from least to greatest:

    −7, 6, −5, −12, 11, 4, 8, −1.

Mid-Year Test
For use after Modules 1–4

53. Refer to the figure at the right.

   a. Use coordinates to describe the transformation that will move the triangle 3 units to the left and 4 units up.

   b. Draw the new image from the translation on the graph paper.

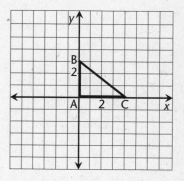

Write each number in scientific notation.

54. 0.0024   **55.** 39,800   **56.** 0.67

Tell whether each set of side lengths can or cannot form a triangle. If they can, tell whether the triangle is *isosceles*, *equilateral*, or *scalene*.

57. 10 in., 8 in., 5 in.   **58.** 7 ft, 5 ft, 7 ft   **59.** 5 cm, 1.3 cm, 2.5 cm

For Questions 60–62, write each fraction as a decimal. Then tell whether the decimal is *terminating* or *repeating*.

60. $\frac{7}{9}$ **61.** $\frac{5}{8}$ **62.** $\frac{6}{4}$

63. Write an equation to represent the following statement, and then solve:

      12 more than 3 times a number is 36.

For Questions 64–66, draw an angle with each measure. Then classify the angle as *acute*, *obtuse*, *right*, or *straight*.

64. $125°$ **65.** $90°$ **66.** $43°$

Answer Key
For use with Module 3

MODULE 3

Diagnostic Test (p. 3-2)

1. B
2. Cannot; 3 + 3 = 6, which is the same length as the third side and will therefore not form a triangle.
3. C
4. Check students' constructions.
5. A
6. D
7. B
8. C
9. B
10. B
11. $\frac{17}{24}$
12. $10\frac{1}{6}$
13. $1\frac{2}{3}$
14. **a.** 2 in.
    b. 2 in.
    c. $1\frac{3}{4}$ in.
15. $1\frac{13}{36}$
16. 5

SECTION 1

Practice and Applications (p. 3-9)

1, 2. Answers were calculated by using 3.14 for π.

1. **a.** 18.84 m **b.** 87.92 cm **c.** 106.76 ft
   d. 56.52 in. **e.** 19.78 cm **f.** 25.75 m
   g. 4.71 ft **h.** 131.88 in. **i.** 53.69 m
2. 34.54 in.
3. **a–c.** Check students' work.
4. **a.** can; scalene **b.** can; isosceles **c.** cannot
   d. can; isosceles **e.** can; isosceles and equilateral **f.** cannot **g.** can; scalene **h.** cannot
5. 11 cm
6. **a.** obtuse **b.** right **c.** acute **d.** right **e.** obtuse
7. $\overline{BE}$

8. $\overline{ZU}$ and $\overline{WR}$
9. $\overline{KQ}$; Sample Response: $\overline{KQ}$ is the only possible answer because it is the only line segment that both crosses $\overline{UN}$ at the point that divides it into two congruent segments and forms right angles where it crosses. Sample Response: $\overline{LR}$ is not a perpendicular bisector of $\overline{UN}$. Even though it crosses $\overline{UN}$ at the same point as $\overline{KQ}$, it does not form a right angle.

Study Guide Exercises (p. 3-14)

1–5. Answers were calculated using the π key on a calculator.

1. 37.70 cm
2. 4.40 mm
3. 47.12 ft
4. 3.14 km
5. 7.23 m
6. can; isosceles
7. cannot
8. can; equilateral
9. can; scalene
10. can; scalene
11. cannot
12. Check students' work; scalene.
13. right
14. obtuse
15. acute
16–19. Check students' work.

Quick Quiz (p. 3-15)

1. Check students' work.
2. No; the two shorter side lengths do not add up to more than the third side-length.
3. **a.** 25.12 ft **b.** 219.8 in.
4. Check students' work.

SECTION 2

Practice and Applications (p. 3-21)

1. **a.** 1, 2, 5, 10 **b.** 1, 2, 7, 14 **c.** 1, 2, 3, 6, 9, 18
   d. 1, 2, 31, 62 **e.** 1, 3, 9, 27, 81 **f.** 1, 2, 7, 14,
   49, 98 **g.** 1, 5, 25, 125 **h.** 1, 13, 169 **i.** 1, 2,
   5, 10, 23, 46, 115, 230

2. **a.** prime **b.** composite **c.** prime
   d. composite **e.** composite **f.** composite
   g. composite **h.** prime **i.** composite

3. **a.** $2 \cdot 3 \cdot 3$ **b.** $2 \cdot 2 \cdot 2 \cdot 3$ **c.** $3 \cdot 3 \cdot 3$
   d. $5 \cdot 7$ **e.** $2 \cdot 19$ **f.** $2 \cdot 2 \cdot 2 \cdot 5$
   g. $5 \cdot 5 \cdot 5$ **h.** $2 \cdot 5 \cdot 11$ **i.** $2 \cdot 3 \cdot 5 \cdot 5$

4. **a.** 6 groups of 13, 3 groups of 26, 2 groups of 39 **b.** 6 groups of 13

5. **a.** 18 in.^{2}, 22 in.; 3 in. by 6 in.; 1 in. by 18 in.
   b. 32 m^2, 36 m; 4 m by 8 m; 1 m by 32 m
   c. 20 ft^2, 24 ft; 4 ft by 5 ft; 1 ft by 20 ft

6. **a.** 5 **b.** 2, 4 **c.** 2 **d.** 2, 3, 6 **e.** 3 **f.** 3, 5, 9
   g. 3, 9 **h.** 2, 5, 10 **i.** none **j.** 2, 3, 4, 5, 6, 10
   k. 2, 4 **l.** 5

7. **a.** 12 **b.** 4 **c.** 5 **d.** 3 **e.** 1 **f.** 14 **g.** 18 **h.** 25
   i. 2 **j.** 3 **k.** 2 **l.** 12 **m.** 8 **n.** 11 **o.** 14

8. Yes; 7650 is divisible by 6.

9. **a.** 20 **b.** 60 **c.** 90 **d.** 75 **e.** 64 **f.** 24 **g.** 378
   h. 250 **i.** 240 **j.** 126 **k.** 288 **l.** 3780

10. **a.** $1.60 **b.** 5 at $0.16 each and 4 at $0.20 each

Study Guide Exercises (p. 3-25)

1. 1, 3, 5, 15

2. 1, 3, 7, 9, 21, 63

3. 1, 2, 4, 5, 7, 10, 14, 20, 28, 35, 70, 140

4. 1, 2, 3, 4, 6, 8, 9, 12, 18, 24, 27, 36, 54, 72, 108, 216

5. C

6. prime

7. prime

8. composite; $2 \cdot 17$

9. composite; $7 \cdot 7 \cdot 7$ or 7^3

10. composite; $2 \cdot 2 \cdot 2 \cdot 2 \cdot 2 \cdot 3$ or $2^5 \cdot 3$

11. prime

12. prime

13. composite; $3 \cdot 7 \cdot 7$ or $3 \cdot 7^2$

14. 88 is divisible by 2 and 4.

15. 405 is divisible by 3, 5, and 9.

16. 540 is divisible by 2, 3, 4, 5, 6, 9, and 10.

17. 435 is divisible by 3 and 5.

18. 2, 3, 6, and 9

19. 2, 4, 5, and 10

20. 2, 3, 4, 6, and 9

21. 5

22. 15

23. 10

24. 1

25. 9

26. 14

27. 21

28. 9

29. 120

30. 45

31. 8 total gumballs
    Sample Response: The least common multiple of 15 and 25 is 75. Fifteen needs to be multiplied by 5 to get 75, and 25 needs to be multiplied by 3. This means he can buy 5 small gumballs and 3 big ones, and spend 75 cents on each.

Quick Quiz (p. 3-26)

1. 1, 2, 3, 4, 5, 6, 8, 10, 12, 15, 16, 20, 24, 30, 40, 48, 60, 80, 120, 240

2. composite

3. $2^4 \cdot 3^2 \cdot 5$

4. 1836 is divisible by 2, 3, 4, 6, and 9.

5. GCF = 12, LCM = 1680

Mid-Module Quiz (p. 3-27)

1. 113.0 mm or 113.1 mm

2. 50.2 mi or 50.3 mi

3. can; isosceles

4. cannot; $7 + 8 = 15$

5. Check students' constructions.

6. Check students' constructions.

7. 1, 2, 41, 82

8. composite; $3 \cdot 57$

9. $3^2 \cdot 5 \cdot 11$

10. 2, 3, 5, 6, 9, 10

11. 8

12. 240

Answer Key

For use with Module 3

SECTION 3

Practice and Applications (p. 3-30)

1. **a.** $\frac{1}{4}$ **b.** $\frac{2}{3}$ **c.** $\frac{3}{7}$ **d.** $\frac{2}{3}$ **e.** $\frac{3}{5}$ **f.** $\frac{5}{6}$ **g.** $\frac{6}{11}$ **h.** $\frac{7}{12}$

   i. $\frac{2}{9}$

2. **a.** greater than **b.** less than **c.** less than

3. **a.** 0 **b.** $\frac{1}{2}$ **c.** 1 **d.** $\frac{1}{2}$ **e.** 0 **f.** 1

4. **a.** > **b.** < **c.** < **d.** = **e.** > **f.** >

5. **a.** $\frac{17}{20}$ **b.** $\frac{7}{8}$ **c.** $\frac{19}{24}$ **d.** $\frac{1}{10}$ **e.** $\frac{17}{36}$ **f.** $\frac{3}{8}$

6. $\frac{5}{24}$

Study Guide Exercises (p. 3-33)

1. $\frac{1}{3}$

2. $\frac{7}{9}$

3. $\frac{2}{3}$

4. $\frac{7}{11}$

5. $\frac{1}{11}$

6. $\frac{2}{3}$

7. $\frac{5}{11}$

8. $\frac{9}{43}$

9. $\frac{7}{10}$

10–15. Sample Responses are given.

10. mental math; <

11. mental math; <

12. paper and pencil; <

13. paper and pencil; <

14. mental math; <

15. paper and pencil; <

16. 0

17. $\frac{38}{45}$

18. $\frac{37}{90}$

19. $\frac{2}{3}$

20. $\frac{11}{12}$

21. $\frac{21}{40}$

22. $\frac{71}{132}$

23. $\frac{5}{6}$

24. $\frac{37}{54}$

25. $\frac{25}{39}$

Quick Quiz (p. 3-34)

1. $\frac{7}{12}$

2. $\frac{4}{9}$

3.

$$\frac{1}{16}, \frac{3}{8}, \frac{7}{16}, \frac{1}{2}, \frac{3}{4}$$

4. 1

5. $\frac{22}{45}$

SECTION 4

Practice and Applications (p. 3-38)

1. **a.** $3\frac{3}{4}$ **b.** $1\frac{4}{5}$ **c.** $3\frac{2}{3}$ **d.** $1\frac{5}{8}$ **e.** $3\frac{2}{3}$ **f.** $4\frac{3}{8}$

2. **a.** $\frac{19}{12}$ **b.** $\frac{17}{6}$ **c.** $\frac{19}{4}$ **d.** $\frac{16}{3}$ **e.** $\frac{75}{8}$ **f.** $\frac{64}{5}$

3. **a.** > **b.** = **c.** > **d.** < **e.** < **f.** >

4. **a.** $3\frac{11}{12}$ **b.** $7\frac{13}{15}$ **c.** $8\frac{7}{8}$ **d.** $5\frac{5}{12}$ **e.** $6\frac{7}{18}$ **f.** $6\frac{3}{4}$

   g. $5\frac{5}{6}$ **h.** $8\frac{1}{8}$ **i.** $12\frac{2}{3}$

5. $6\frac{3}{4}$ mi

6. **a.** $14\frac{1}{8}$ yd **b.** $3\frac{11}{24}$ yd

7. **a–f.** Check students' work.

8. **a.** 2 in. **b.** $5\frac{1}{4}$ in. **c.** $3\frac{1}{2}$ in. **d.** $\frac{3}{4}$ in.

   e. $4\frac{1}{2}$ in. **f.** $1\frac{1}{4}$ in.

9. **a.** 3520 **b.** 48 **c.** 18 **d.** 6 **e.** $2\frac{1}{2}$ **f.** 36
    g. $4\frac{1}{2}$ **h.** 26 **i.** $17\frac{1}{9}$ **j.** $9\frac{2}{3}$ **k.** $7\frac{13}{16}$ **l.** $1\frac{1}{4}$

10. **a.** 204 in. **b.** $5\frac{2}{3}$ yd **c.** 3 giraffes

11. **a.** $32\frac{1}{2}$ yd **b.** $97\frac{1}{2}$ ft **c.** 1170 in.

Study Guide Exercises (p. 3-43)

1. $9\frac{1}{4}$

2. $6\frac{5}{6}$

3. $9\frac{2}{3}$

4. $10\frac{5}{12}$

5. $\frac{11}{4}$

6. $\frac{83}{7}$

7. $\frac{23}{3}$

8. Sample Response: $\frac{6}{1}$

9. $6\frac{1}{6}$

10. $13\frac{3}{4}$

11. $7\frac{7}{18}$

12. $5\frac{1}{6}$

13. $2\frac{1}{9}$

14. $6\frac{8}{77}$

15. $5\frac{3}{4}$

16. $2\frac{19}{60}$

17. $12\frac{26}{45}$

18. $3\frac{5}{6}$

19. $6\frac{15}{22}$

20. $6\frac{1}{3}$

21. $21\frac{13}{18}$

22. $25\frac{3}{16}$

23. $1\frac{37}{50}$

24. $3\frac{7}{48}$

25. $13\frac{7}{12}$

26. $5\frac{8}{15}$

27. $3\frac{1}{2} + 4\frac{2}{3} + x = 14$; $x = 5\frac{5}{6}$ in.

28. **a.** 1320 ft **b.** 440 yd

29. two times

Quick Quiz (p. 3-44)

1. $5\frac{1}{4}$

2. $\frac{231}{100}$

3. $7\frac{2}{3}$

4. $4\frac{11}{14}$

5. $1\frac{3}{8}$ yd

END-OF-MODULE RESOURCES AND ASSESSMENTS

Practice and Applications, Sections 1–4 (p. 3-45)

1. **a.** 4 cm **b.** 2 cm **c.** 12.57 cm

2. **a.** equilateral **b.** isosceles **c.** scalene

3. **a.** right **b.** obtuse **c.** acute

4. Check students' work.

5. **a.** 1, 23 **b.** 1, 2, 3, 4, 6, 9, 12, 18, 36
    c. 1, 3, 5, 9, 15, 45

6. **a.** prime **b.** composite **c.** composite
    d. composite **e.** prime **f.** composite

7. **a.** $2 \cdot 3 \cdot 7$ **b.** $2 \cdot 2 \cdot 2 \cdot 7$ **c.** $5 \cdot 13$

8. **a.** > **b.** < **c.** < **d.** > **e.** > **f.** <

9. **a.** $\frac{2}{9}$ **b.** $\frac{7}{24}$ **c.** $\frac{14}{15}$ **d.** $\frac{13}{24}$ **e.** $\frac{7}{33}$ **f.** $\frac{23}{36}$

Math Thematics, Book 2
Teacher's Resource Book, Modules 3 and 4

10. $\frac{17}{24}$

11. **a.** $5\frac{2}{9}$ **b.** $2\frac{4}{15}$ **c.** $21\frac{5}{6}$ **d.** $16\frac{7}{12}$ **e.** $4\frac{1}{4}$

   f. $10\frac{5}{12}$ **g.** $53\frac{3}{4}$ **h.** $21\frac{1}{5}$ **i.** $14\frac{7}{30}$

12. **a.** 90 **b.** 48 **c.** $\frac{3}{4}$ **d.** 102 **e.** 3 **f.** $\frac{1}{2}$

13. **a.** > **b.** < **c.** > **d.** < **e.** < **f.** =

Test Form A (p. 3-47)

1. can; isosceles
2. cannot
3. can; scalene
4. 62.80 ft or 62.38 ft
5. 9.42 in.
6. Check students' constructions.
7. Check students' constructions.
8. $2^4 \cdot 3^2$
9. $5 \cdot 13$
10. 5
11. 4
12. 30
13. 448
14. >
15. =
16. <
17. Sample Response: $\frac{13}{20}$ is in lowest terms because the only common factor of 13 and 20 is 1.
18. **a.** 2 in.

   b. $1\frac{1}{2}$ in.

   c. $1\frac{3}{4}$ in.
19. $3\frac{1}{3}$
20. 33
21. $8\frac{3}{4}$
22. not possible
23. $1\frac{3}{10}$
24. $2\frac{5}{8}$

25. $13\frac{23}{25}$

Test Form B (p. 3-49)

1. cannot
2. can; isosceles
3. can; scalene
4. 31.40 ft or 31.42 ft
5. 34.54 in. or 34.56 in.
6. Check students' constructions.
7. Check students' constructions.
8. $2^2 \cdot 3^2 \cdot 5$
9. $3 \cdot 5^2$
10. 5
11. 14
12. 75
13. 280
14. >
15. <
16. =
17. Sample Response: $\frac{11}{20}$ is in lowest terms because the only common factor of 11 and 20 is 1.
18. **a.** 2 in.

   b. 2 in.

   c. $2\frac{1}{4}$ in.
19. 3
20. 27
21. $6\frac{3}{4}$
22. not possible
23. $\frac{31}{20}$ or $1\frac{11}{20}$
24. $\frac{47}{8}$ or $5\frac{7}{8}$
25. $\frac{104}{15}$ or $6\frac{14}{15}$

Standardized Test (p. 3-51)

1. c
2. b
3. a
4. d

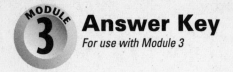

5. c

6. c

7. c

8. a

9. b

10. c

11. b

12. c

Performance Assessment (p. 3-52)

Step 1: 1 pack of 60 pieces; 2 packs of 30 pieces; 3 packs of 20 pieces; 4 packs of 15 pieces; 5 packs of 12 pieces; 6 packs of 10 pieces; 10 packs of 6 pieces; 12 packs of 5 pieces; 15 packs of 4 pieces; 20 packs of 3 pieces; 30 packs of 2 pieces; 60 packs of 1 piece

Step 2:

$$\frac{P}{3} = s$$

$$\frac{P}{3} = 9.5$$

$$P = 28.5$$

Step 3: The piece is probably too large to be used in most smaller jewelry, such as earrings, rings, or bracelets. It could be used in a necklace, though.

Step 4: The sum of the lengths of any two sides of a triangle is greater than the length of the remaining side.

Since $8\frac{1}{4} + 4\frac{3}{8} = 12\frac{5}{8}$ and $12\frac{5}{8}$ is less than $12\frac{3}{4}$, the measurements cannot describe a triangle.

Step 5: She should use the 3-inch triangles. Sample Response: 3 feet is the same as 36 inches. The only choice that 36 is divisible by is 3.

Answer Key
For use with Module 4

MODULE 4

Diagnostic Test (p. 4-2)

1. D
2. A
3. B
4. B
5. D
6. C
7. C
8. A
9. A
10. B
11. D
12. C
13. 4
14. −40
15. 48
16. D
17. D
18. 29; 141 = 141
19. 36; 19 = 19

SECTION 1

Practice and Applications (p. 4-11)

1. **a.** $\frac{1}{10}$ **b.** $\frac{1}{3}$ **c.** $\frac{3}{5}$ **d.** $\frac{5}{8}$ **e.** $\frac{4}{9}$ **f.** $\frac{1}{40}$

   g. $10\frac{1}{2}$ **h.** $7\frac{4}{5}$ **i.** $14\frac{7}{32}$ **j.** $\frac{3}{10}$ **k.** $\frac{3}{8}$

   l. $\frac{1}{15}$ **m.** $\frac{4}{15}$ **n.** $\frac{2}{3}$ **o.** $\frac{1}{9}$

2. $1\frac{1}{16}$ yd

3. $\frac{5}{14}$ lb

4. **a.** 5 **b.** $\frac{6}{13}$ **c.** $\frac{1}{27}$ **d.** $\frac{7}{6}$ **e.** $\frac{5}{18}$ **f.** $\frac{6}{5}$ **g.** $\frac{6}{17}$

   h. $\frac{3}{14}$ **i.** $\frac{1}{8}$ **j.** $\frac{9}{2}$ **k.** $\frac{7}{8}$ **l.** $\frac{1}{13}$ **m.** $\frac{3}{19}$ **n.** $\frac{4}{9}$ **o.** $\frac{11}{5}$

5. **a.** 2 **b.** $9\frac{3}{5}$ **c.** $\frac{5}{9}$ **d.** 11 **e.** $8\frac{1}{4}$ **f.** $3\frac{13}{24}$

   g. $2\frac{1}{7}$ **h.** $2\frac{1}{6}$ **i.** 10 **j.** $3\frac{5}{7}$ **k.** 18 **l.** 2 **m.** $2\frac{2}{7}$

n. $5\frac{1}{3}$ **o.** $2\frac{2}{3}$ **p.** $13\frac{3}{5}$ **q.** $1\frac{3}{5}$ **r.** $1\frac{5}{9}$ **s.** $1\frac{19}{45}$

t. 10 **u.** $5\frac{1}{3}$

6. **a.** 4 pieces **b.** No.
7. **a.** 10 pieces **b.** Yes; $\frac{1}{4}$ of a piece or $\frac{3}{8}$ lb is left over.
8. **a.** $8\frac{5}{12}$ c **b.** $50\frac{1}{2}$ c

Study Guide Exercises (p. 4-15)

1. $\frac{4}{63}$
2. $2\frac{1}{2}$
3. $\frac{1}{16}$
4. 23
5. 1
6. $5\frac{1}{2}$
7. $\frac{5}{18}$
8. $\frac{38}{45}$
9. $\frac{32}{11}$
10. $\frac{1}{8}$
11. $\frac{3}{2}$
12. $\frac{8}{5}$
13. $\frac{5}{23}$
14. $\frac{9}{49}$
15. $\frac{48}{7}$
16. $\frac{1}{21}$
17. $\frac{8}{57}$
18. $\frac{5}{16}$
19. $\frac{3}{7}$
20. $\frac{16}{33}$

Math Thematics, Book 2

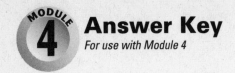

Answer Key

For use with Module 4

21. $\frac{2}{9}$

22. $\frac{5}{8}$

23. $\frac{1}{38}$

24. $\frac{15}{4}$

25. $\frac{2}{3}$

26. 15

27. 1

28. $\frac{1}{3}$

29. $1\frac{1}{2}$

30. $4\frac{5}{18}$

31. $\frac{5}{6}$

32. $\frac{7}{72}$

33. $15\frac{5}{7}$

34. $2\frac{4}{9}$

35. 24

36. $\frac{5}{24}$

Quick Quiz (p. 4-16)

1. $\frac{1}{4}$

2. $8\frac{4}{17}$

3. a. $\frac{5}{6}$ b. $\frac{5}{13}$ c. $\frac{1}{17}$

4. $4\frac{1}{2}$

5. Sample Response: a. $\frac{5}{8} \cdot \frac{8}{5}$ b. $\frac{11}{12} \div \frac{11}{12}$

SECTION 2

Practice and Applications (p. 4-18)

1. a–c. Check students' work.

2. a. 2.00 mm b. 0.6 m c. 13.7 cm d. 8.5 m

3. a. 4 b. 36,000 c. 92.1 d. 0.9 e. 180,000
f. 0.0278 g. 0.000071 h. 600,000,000
i. 76,300 j. 25.6

4. a. > b. = c. > d. < e. < f. < g. < h. >

5. 1.5 m; 150 cm

Study Guide Exercises (p. 4-21)

1. C
2. A
3. C
4. B
5. A
6. 31,500
7. 2300
8. 81.12
9. 0.00007
10. 0.001256
11. 0.701
12. 6200
13. 0.00506
14. 150,000
15. 0.000306
16. >
17. <
18. <
19. =
20. <
21. =
22. a. 6.6 km b. 6600 m

Quick Quiz (p. 4-22)

1. 82,000 cm
2. greater than
3. 70 m tall by 8 m wide at the base
4. 2.14 m
5. Unreasonable; that would be higher than a 2-story building (1 story ≈ 3 m), or about 4 times the height of a classroom door.

Math Thematics, Book 2
Teacher's Resource Book, Modules 3 and 4

Answer Key

For use with Module 4

SECTION 3

Practice and Applications (p. 4-24)

1. **a.** 1.098 **b.** 28.683 **c.** 1.93848 **d.** 1745.055
2. **a.** 139.916 **b.** 0.189 **c.** 65.16 **d.** 159.505
   e. 1.22235 **f.** 0.1598 **g.** 16.598
   h. 0.0515 **i.** 3.3726
3. **a.** less than; $0 < 0.46 < 1$ **b.** greater than;
   $1.59 > 1$ **c.** Equal to; any number multiplied
   by 1 is the number itself.
4. $10.91
5. **a.** 712.5 **b.** 14.5 **c.** 42.5 **d.** 25.5
6. **a.** 8 **b.** 7.5 **c.** 0.43 **d.** 7.2 **e.** 14,000 **f.** 3.6
   g. 5.4 **h.** 6.8 **i.** 3.25
7. 60 m
8. **a.** 0.269269 **b.** 4.717171 **c.** 0.043333
   d. 21.535353 **e.** 1.040404 **f.** 6.188888
   g. 3.102102 **h.** 123.656565 **i.** 4.127777
   j. 19.222222 **k.** 1.762626 **l.** 1.809809
9. **a.** $0.9\overline{6}$ **b.** $32.\overline{8}$ **c.** $0.\overline{592}$ **d.** $0.1\overline{5}$
   e. undefined **f.** $759.\overline{09}$ **g.** 0 **h.** $4.\overline{7}$ **i.** $115.\overline{45}$
10. **a.** 0.38 **b.** 0.17 **c.** 0.78 **d.** 0.57 **e.** 0.22
    f. 0.42 **g.** 0.33 **h.** 0.27 **i.** 0.83 **j.** 0.55
    k. 0.71 **l.** 0.88 **m.** 0.92 **n.** 0.44 **o.** 0.73
11. **a.** greater than; $0 < 0.29 < 1$ **b.** less than;
    $174 > 1$ **c.** Equal to; any number divided
    by 1 is the number itself. **d.** greater than;
    $0 < 0.92 < 1$ **e.** less than; $2163 > 1$ **f.** less
    than; $53.4 > 1$ **g.** greater than; $0 < 0.5 < 1$
    h. less than; $6 > 1$ **i.** less than; $1.9 > 1$
12. The photographs must be about 26.7% of
    their original size.

Study Guide Exercises (p. 4-28)

1. 0.1666
2. 59.8
3. 5.9808
4. 0.0448
5. 1572.87
6. 0.0584
7. 2535.39
8. 2.06515
9. 0.1638

10. 22.8
11. 0.7982
12. 0.2356
13. 331.5
14. 0.0504
15. 2571.27
16. $4.63
17. 15.2
18. 3.2
19. 3.8
20. 6.3
21. 120,000
22. 0.98
23. 10
24. 1100
25. 64.1
26. 10.9
27. 20
28. 20.3
29. $1.\overline{6}$
30. $5.\overline{185}$
31. undefined
32. $0.3\overline{5}$
33. 0
34. $153.4\overline{09}$
35. 0.86
36. 0.44
37. 0.42
38. 0.11
39. 0.38
40. 0.27
41. 0.17
42. 0.31
43. 0.88

Quick Quiz (p. 4-29)

1. 1074.015
2. 16.128
3. 1487.333...
4. 0.363636...; repeating
5. **a–b.** Answers will vary. **c.** 89.523

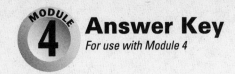

Answer Key

For use with Module 4

Mid-Module Quiz (p. 4-30)

1. $36\frac{1}{2}$

2. $14\frac{2}{9}$

3. $\frac{7}{6}$

4. $\frac{8}{19}$

5. $\frac{4}{11}$

6. $\frac{16}{3}$ or $5\frac{1}{3}$

7. $\frac{35}{48}$

8. $\frac{20}{21}$

9. 6.7 cm

10. A

11. 2600

12. 34.5

13. Answers will vary; about $100 \div 0.1 = 1000$.

14. Answers will vary; about $40 \cdot 0.02 = 0.8$.

15. 640

16. 0.615

17. $0.0\overline{6}$

18. 0.7777

19. 0.6499999

20. 0.3143143

SECTION 4

Practice and Applications (p. 4-35)

1. **a.** Yes; 120°, 240° **b.** Yes; 90°, 180°, 270°
   c. Yes; 180° **d.** Yes; 90°, 180°, 270°
   e. No. **f.** Yes; 180°

2. **a.** Yes. **b.** No. **c.** Yes.

3. **a.** Yes. **b.** No. **c.** Yes.

4. **a.** Yes. **b.** No. One half of the figure is not a reflection of the other half. **c.** No. One half of the figure is not a reflection of the other half.

Study Guide Exercises (p. 4-38)

1. Check students' work.

2. No.

3. Yes; 120° and 240°.

4. Yes; 180°.

5. No.

6. Yes.

7. No.

8. Yes.

9. No.

10. Yes.

11. Yes.

12. Yes.

13. No. One half of the figure is not a reflection of the other half.

14. Yes.

Quick Quiz (p. 4-39)

1. 180°

2. Yes.

3. No; if folded along the line, the two parts of the figure do not match.

4. Yes.

SECTION 5

Practice and Applications (p. 4-45)

1. **a.** –21 **b.** –60 **c.** –54 **d.** 20 **e.** –126 **f.** –106
   g. –240 **h.** –144 **i.** 125 **j.** –105 **k.** 128 **l.** –360

2. **a.** $-9x = 45$; –5 **b.** $3x = -18$; –6
   c. $-2x = -8$; 4 **d.** $25x = -25$; –1
   e. $-12x = 48$; –4 **f.** $7x = -42$; –6

3. **a.** –6 **b.** –6 **c.** 7 **d.** –7 **e.** 24 **f.** –24 **g.** –15
   h. –11 **i.** 28 **j.** –40 **k.** –50 **l.** –25

4. **a.** –60 **b.** 52 **c.** –360 **d.** 210 **e.** 360 **f.** 8000

5. **a.** –7 **b.** –90 **c.** –30 **d.** –738 **e.** 16 **f.** –90

6. –15°C

7. **a.** –140 **b.** $1\frac{1}{4}$ **c.** 4.8 **d.** $17\frac{2}{9}$ **e.** 29.5
   f. 839.52 **g.** 3.4 **h.** 7 **i.** –66

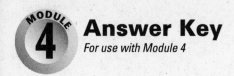

8. a. $4\frac{4}{5}$ b. $5\frac{1}{3}$ c. $3\frac{1}{4}$ d. $5\frac{1}{6}$ e. 18 f. $9\frac{1}{3}$ g. $6\frac{2}{5}$
   h. -3 i. $25\frac{1}{3}$

9. a. 12.8 b. 8 c. 16.8 d. 15 e. 5.2 f. 0.6
   g. 32 h. 2 i. 1.12

10. a. 38 b. 10 c. 31 d. -9.5 e. 14 f. -27
    g. -20 h. 10.5 i. 22 j. -11 k. 2 l. -25

11. a. $0.5 + 0.15x$ b. \$2.75

Study Guide Exercises (p. 4-48)

1. -30
2. -48
3. 9
4. -110
5. 28
6. -38
7. -5
8. -20
9. 9
10. -56
11. 7
12. 65
13. -51
14. -9
15. -35
16. $-21°C$
17. $-\$60$
18. -1
19. $1\frac{1}{4}$
20. $-2\frac{2}{5}$
21. 16.18
22. -264
23. 12.73
24. $-1\frac{2}{5}$
25. 5.3
26. 5.6
27. -2
28. 41
29. 25

30. 1
31. 1.5
32. -30
33. Sample Response: At noon the temperature was 3° less than twice the temperature at midnight. If the temperature at midnight was 5°, what was the temperature at noon? (Answer: 7°)

Quick Quiz (p. 4-49)

1. 40
2. -20
3. $4\frac{1}{4}$
4. $-2 \cdot (3 + (-1)) \div (6 - 8) = 2$
5. 1.216 or $1\frac{216}{1000}$

SECTION 6

Practice and Applications (p. 4-54)

1. a. Yes. b. No; the figure has been rotated. c. Yes.

2. a. $(x - 5, y)$ b. $(x, y - 8)$ c. $(x, y + 6)$
   d. $(x + 4, y)$ e. $(x + 2, y + 6)$ f. $(x - 3, y - 5)$
   g. $(x - 5, y + 1)$ h. $(x + 7, y - 4)$

3. a. Check students' work. The image of the original rectangle should be 2 units to the right and 1 unit below the original. b. Check students' work. The image of the original rectangle should be 3 units to the left and 2 units below the original.

4. a. No; the figure is squashed horizontally and stretched vertically. b. No; there is only horizontal stretching. c. Yes; the figure is squashed the same amount horizontally and vertically. d. No; the figure is squashed different amounts horizontally and vertically. e. Yes; the figure is stretched the same amount horizontally and vertically. f. No; there is only vertical stretching. g. No; the figure is stretched horizontally and squashed vertically. h. No; the figure is stretched different amounts horizontally and vertically.

5.

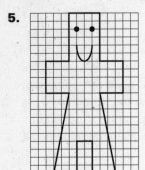

6. a. 5 **b.** 32 **c.** –6 **d.** 1.8 **e.** 0 **f.** $-1\frac{1}{6}$

g. 196 **h.** $2\frac{3}{5}$ **i.** 48.8 **j.** 7 **k.** –36

l. 6.3 **m.** $1\frac{3}{4}$ **n.** 360 **o.** –8

7. a. $3n + 5 = 32$; 9 **b.** $\frac{n}{4} - 6 = 6$; 48

c. $8 + 7n = 43$; 5 **d.** $6n + 9 = 81$; 12

e. $\frac{n}{5} - 4 = 3$; 35 **f.** $12 + 2n = 28$; 8

8. a. $c = 35 + 8x$ **b.** 4 days

9. a. $3x - 5 = 43$ **b.** $16

Study Guide Exercises (p. 4-58)

1. No; Sample Response: the figure has been rotated.

2. Yes.

3. Yes.

4. $(x - 8, y - 1)$

5. $(x + 5, y + 3)$

6. Check students' work; the image should be 4 units to the right and 3 units down from the original figure.

7. A and D

8. Check students' work; the transformation should be stretched horizontally by a factor of 2 and squashed vertically by a factor of $\frac{1}{2}$.

9. No.

10. Yes.

11. No.

12. $t = 8$

13. $m = -50$

14. $x = 3$

15. $x = 22$

16. $y = 25$

17. $m = 3$

18. $t = -10$

19. $x = 7$

20. $y = -6$

Quick Quiz (p. 4-59)

1. $(x + 2, y - 5)$

2. B

3. Check students' work. Sample Response: $\left(2x, \frac{y}{2}\right)$

4. $t = 11$

5. a. $6 + \frac{n}{4} = 36$ **b.** $n = 120$

END-OF-MODULE RESOURCES AND ASSESSMENTS

Practice and Applications, Sections 1–6 (p. 4-60)

1. a. $8\frac{2}{3}$ **b.** $\frac{1}{4}$ **c.** $3\frac{23}{40}$

2. a. $7\frac{1}{5}$ **b.** $1\frac{6}{7}$ **c.** $3\frac{2}{3}$

3. a. 3,000,000 **b.** 0.85 **c.** 0.055 **d.** 0.063

4. a. = **b.** < **c.** > **d.** <

5. a. 0.068 **b.** 486.16 **c.** 5.436

6. a. greater than; $1.2 > 1$ **b.** less than; $0.95 < 1$ **c.** Equal to; any number multiplied by 1 is the number itself.

7. a. 0.21 **b.** 0.56 **c.** 0.58

8. a. greater than; $0 < 0.32 < 1$ **b.** less than; $118 > 1$ **c.** Equal to; any number divided by 1 is the number itself.

9. a. No. **b.** Yes. **c.** Yes.

10. a. –12 **b.** –42 **c.** –70 **d.** –608 **e.** 24 **f.** –72

11. –16°C

12. a. 36 **b.** –25 **c.** 2 **d.** –9 **e.** 10 **f.** –2

13. a. $(x + 7, y + 1)$ **b.** $(x - 2, y - 8)$

14. a. No; the figure is squashed horizontally and stretched vertically. **b.** No; there is only horizontal stretching. **c.** Yes; the figure is stretched the same amount horizontally and vertically.

15. a. 8 **b.** 55 **c.** −8

16. $8 + 6n = 50$; 7

Test Form A (p. 4-67)

1. $\dfrac{3}{2}$

2. $\dfrac{4}{9}$

3. $\dfrac{5}{6}$

4. $\dfrac{1}{6}$

5. $2\dfrac{2}{5}$

6. 2

7. unreasonable; 15 cm or 150 mm

8. reasonable

9. 2500

10. 310,000

11. 0.357

12. $49.\overline{3}$

13. 3.515

14. 803.75

15. $1.\overline{4}$

16. 0.15

17. Sample Response: A terminating decimal has a finite number of decimal places; 1.53. In a repeating decimal one or more of the digits in the decimal repeats; 3.575757... or $3.\overline{57}$.

18. Yes; 180°

19. Yes; it is a reflection.

20. −28

21. −10

22. 88

23. 4

24. 5

25. −11

26. **a.** $(x − 2, y − 4)$

b.
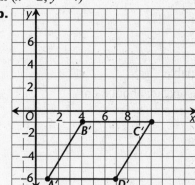

27. **a.** The figure will be one third the original width and two times the height. It will remain a parallelogram, but the image will be shifted to the left.

b. Image coordinates are $A'(1, −4)$, $B'(2, 6)$, $C'(4, 6)$, $D'(3, −4)$.

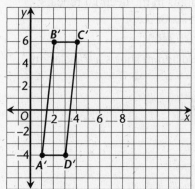

c. No; the ratios of corresponding sides are not the same.

28. 15; $8(15) − 3 = 117$, $117 = 117$

29. 8; $\dfrac{8}{4} + 3 = 5$; $5 = 5$

Test Form B (p. 4-69)

1. $\dfrac{8}{5}$

2. $\dfrac{7}{22}$

3. $1\dfrac{3}{11}$

4. $\frac{3}{8}$

5. $2\frac{2}{3}$

6. $3\frac{3}{8}$

7. reasonable

8. unreasonable; about 8 cm

9. 4.2

10. 3.8

11. 7200

12. 41.75

13. 1.238

14. 2030

15. $1.\overline{6}$

16. 0.55

17. Sample Response: A terminating decimal has a finite number of decimal places; 1.53. In a repeating decimal one or more of the digits in the decimal repeats; 3.575757... or $3.\overline{57}$.

18. Yes; 120°, 240°

19. No; the diagram shows a translation.

20. −140

21. −5

22. 24

23. 4

24. 8

25. −4

26. **a.** $(x + 3, y + 5)$

b.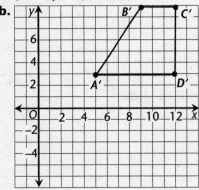

27. **a.** The figure will be one half the original width and three times its height. It will remain a right trapezoid, but the figure will be shifted to the left.

b. Image coordinates are $A'(1, -6)$, $B'(3, 12)$, $C'(4.5, 12)$, $D'(4.5, -6)$.

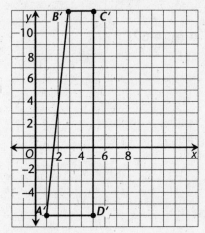

c. No; the ratios of corresponding sides are not the same.

28. 12; 65 = 65

29. −80; −5 = −5

Standardized Test (p. 4-71)

1. b

2. c

3. c

4. a

5. c

6. d

7. c

8. d

9. c

10. c

11. b

12. c

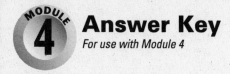

Answer Key

For use with Module 4

Performance Assessment (p. 4-72)

Step 1: The figure has 3 lines of symmetry. It has rotational symmetries of 120° and 240°.

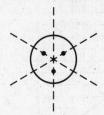

Step 2: The circumference is about 4.71 cm.

Step 3: $8 \div 1.5 = 5.\overline{3}$; since this is a repeating decimal, the animator may have to use an enlargement of 5.33 instead.

Step 4: No. Dividing by a fraction less than 1 is the same as multiplying by its reciprocal, which will be greater than 1 and actually expand the figure, not shrink it.

Step 5:

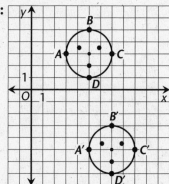

Yes, it is a translation. No, it is not a reflection. If the figure were reflected over the x-axis, the points would still have the same x-coordinate.

Step 6: a. Image I: $\left(\frac{3}{2}x, \frac{3}{2}y\right)$; Image II: $\left(\frac{x}{2}, x\right)$;

Image III: $(x, 2y)$ **b.** Only Image I is similar to the original figure.

Answer Key

For use after Modules 3 and 4

Modules 3 and 4 Cumulative Test (p. CT-1)

1. can; scalene
2. 56.5 in.
3. 251.2 ft
4. Check students' constructions.
5. $2 \cdot 3 \cdot 5 \cdot 7$
6. 22
7. 60
8. $<$
9. $=$
10. $4\frac{7}{8}$
11. $2\frac{11}{18}$
12. $\frac{7}{2}$ or $3\frac{1}{2}$
13. $\frac{7}{6}$ or $1\frac{1}{6}$
14. $\frac{27}{4}$ or $6\frac{3}{4}$
15. $0.3\overline{6}$; repeating
16. $5\frac{1}{3}$
17. 54
18. 0.15
19. 5150
20. 0.0039
21. -15
22. 96
23. line symmetry:

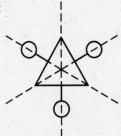

rotational symmetries: 120°, 240°

24. 896; $112 = 112$
25. -4; $-23 = -23$
26. **a.** $(x - 2, y + 5)$

   b.

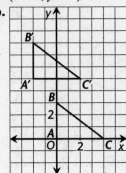

Answer Key

For use after Modules 1–4

Mid-Year Test (p. MYT-1)

1. 5
2. –4
3. –6
4. –10
5. $6\frac{7}{8}$
6. $6\frac{1}{6}$
7. $3\frac{3}{8}$
8. $2\frac{3}{4}$
9. $\frac{9}{40}$
10. $9\frac{1}{2}$
11. $1\frac{1}{6}$
12. 3
13. –35
14. 48
15. –8
16. –41
17. 1,236,000
18. 0.01236
19. 0.001236
20. 1236
21. 0.252
22. 55.5
23. 7185
24. $4.\overline{1}$
25. 7
26. 14
27. 21
28. 14
29. 4
30. –1
31. =
32. <
33. >
34. $y = 9$

35. $x = -22$
36. $z = 8$
37. $y = 16$
38. $x = 252$
39. $b = 8$
40. 36
41. –5
42. 6
43. 20
44. $\frac{1}{2}$
45. 4
46. $\frac{1}{3}$
47. 60°
48. **a.**

Term number	1	2	3	4	...	n
Outcome	4	8	12	16	...	$4n$

   b.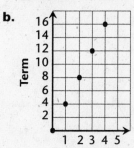

   c. Let t = the term, let n = the term number; $t = 4n$

   d. 400

49.

Spinner A	Spinner B		
	0	2	4
1	1	3	5
3	3	5	7
5	5	7	9

50. $P(1) = \frac{1}{9}$, $P(3) = \frac{2}{9}$, $P(5) = \frac{1}{3}$, $P(7) = \frac{2}{9}$, $P(9) = \frac{1}{9}$

51. 30 times
52. –12, –7, –5, –1, 4, 6, 8, 11

Answer Key

For use after Modules 1–4

53. **a.** $(x - 3, y + 4)$

b.

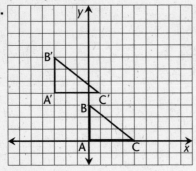

54. 2.4×10^{-3}

55. 3.98×10^4

56. 6.7×10^{-1}

57. can; scalene

58. can; isosceles

59. cannot

60. $0.\overline{7}$, repeating

61. 0.625; terminating

62. 1.5; terminating

63. $12 + 3x = 36$; $x = 8$

64. obtuse

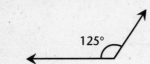

65. right

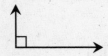

66. acute

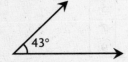